Puzzles for
Mindfulness

Puzzles for
Mindfulness

A wonderful collection to
help you de-stress

This edition published in 2021 by Arcturus Publishing Limited
26/27 Bickels Yard, 151–153 Bermondsey Street,
London SE1 3HA

AD008529NT

Printed in the UK

Contents

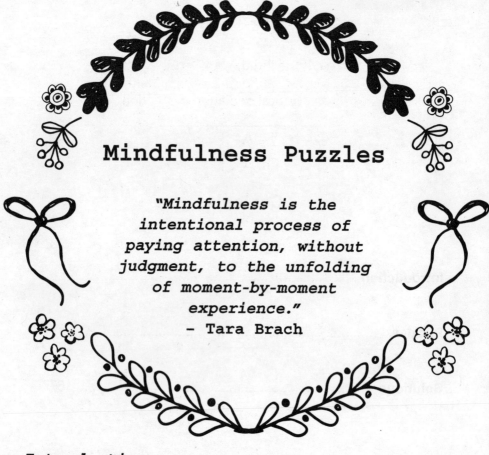

Mindfulness Puzzles

"Mindfulness is the intentional process of paying attention, without judgment, to the unfolding of moment-by-moment experience."
- Tara Brach

Introduction

Mindfulness is the art of being in the moment. People often think that this involves some complex meditative process but actually it is much simpler than that. To begin mindfulness requires only that you choose to become more mindful. You choose to take a moment, any moment, each and every day, take a deep breath, and experience everything that is unfolding right now, exactly as it is.

If you struggle to switch off and focus on the moment, the puzzles in this book can help by giving your mind a peaceful and absorbing pastime to concentrate on. There are various sorts of puzzles contained within, some will be familiar to you, and some may not. Try them all as the variety will help to keep your mind engaged, and you may discover new ones that you love! There are also insightful and uplifting quotes dotted throughout to inspire you on your mindfulness journey. So, turn the page to begin that journey, we hope it brings you joy.

Can you find all of the listed words hidden in the grid?
They may run forward or backward, in either a
horizontal, vertical or diagonal direction.

```
E E D J C I T A T S C E E D D
C S Q X N E D A Y G Z A T A E
X U W E J N E I K K P Y T L L
Y N N U U M U N Z L R B E G B
L N M C B A P G C U U E O E U
L Y O X J U H L N U R C P L O
O J P P Y Y O U E I P Y K L R
J M P D I K R Y E A L B O Y T
O O R N E D I P A E S I E Q N
V S Y A Z L C M V N T E M A U
I I C F D E L I G H T E D S T
A A F N U I L I C O N T E N T
L W L A Q L A Y R D E T A L E
N S M E R R Y N E H T I L B E
G N I H G U A L T M T N A B E
```

BLITHE	JOCUND	PERKY
BUOYANT	JOLLY	PLEASED
CONTENT	JOVIAL	RADIANT
DELIGHTED	JOYFUL	SMILING
ECSTATIC	LAUGHING	SUNNY
ELATED	LIVELY	THRILLED
EUPHORIC	LUCKY	UNTROUBLED
GLAD	MERRY	UPBEAT

Criss Cross: BUNCH OF FLOWERS

The words are provided, but can you fit them all in the grid?

4 letters
IRIS
LILY

5 letters
ASTER
DAISY
LILAC
LUPIN
TANSY
TULIP

6 letters
CROCUS
SALVIA

7 letters
GENTIAN
NIGELLA
PETUNIA

8 letters
LAVENDER
SNOWDROP
XANTHIUM

9 letters
AQUILEGIA
CALENDULA
CELANDINE
COLUMBINE

10 letters
SNAPDRAGON

15 letters
MICHAELMAS
DAISY

Discover a path to the image in the middle of this maze. Start at the entrance at the top.

"Mindfulness is a way of befriending ourselves and our experience."

Jon Kabat-Zinn

4   Patchwork Quilt

Place all twelve of the pieces into the grid. Any may be rotated or flipped over, but none may touch another, not even diagonally.

The numbers outside the grid refer to the number of consecutive black squares; and each block is separated from the others by at least one white square. For instance, '3 2' could refer to a row with none, one or more white squares, then three black squares, then at least one white square, then two more black squares, followed by any number of white squares.

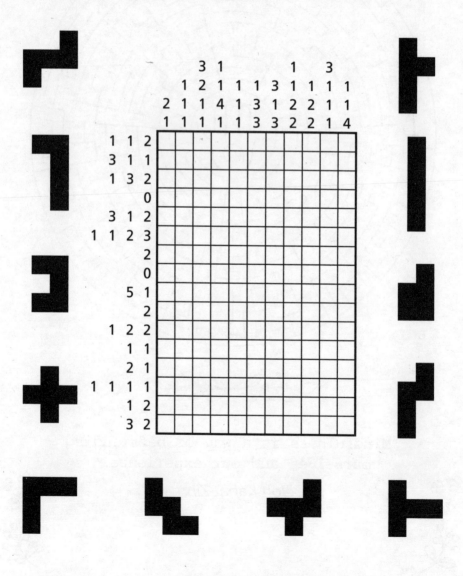

Can you find all of the listed words hidden in the grid?
They may run forward or backward, in either a
horizontal, vertical or diagonal direction.

```
K Z T C Y F D O W S I N G X M
P M I Y G B C R P S U F M S I
R T B K O A V I A M E L I A N
I H E B L P L W S M A M B C A
M E T Y O U O V X U A K J H N
A R A M I A S L A H M X W E U
L B N O S B O T A N I C A L L
K A N N E X A R A R I J A A Z
D L B O N I G G L I I S D T A
L N M G I Q K L O S H T M I N
L Z U R K S D I E Y O S Y O A
R Z H O Y W I I E Q I G O N G
L O F V S W T V B R G G D U A
E N B M B A G N V Q A R T N Q
B E C M I Z O W P I L A T E S
```

BOTANICAL	KINESIOLOGY	SEITAI
CHELATION	MUSIC	SHIATSU
DOWSING	ORGONOMY	SOUND
DRAMA	PILATES	TIBETAN
GALVANISM	POLARITY	UNANI
GRAHAMISM	PRIMAL	VISION
HERBAL	QIGONG	YOGA
KAMPO	REIKI	ZONE

The words are provided, but can you fit them all in the grid?

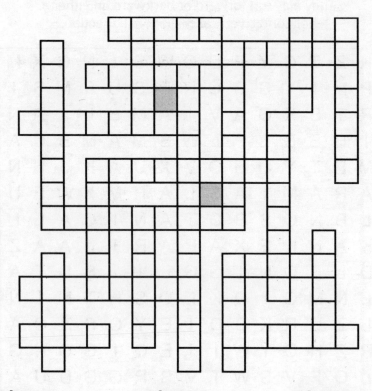

4 letters
PINE
ROSE

5 letters
BASIL
ELEMI
MANGO
MYRRH
PEONY
THYME

6 letters
ALMOND
GINGER
MIMOSA
NUTMEG

7 letters
BAY LEAF
FREESIA

8 letters
BLUEBELL
CARDAMOM
GERANIUM
MARJORAM
ROSEMARY

9 letters
AMBERGRIS
LEMON BALM

13 letters
SAMARKAND
MUSK

Place one of the numbers from 1 to 9 into every
empty cell so that each row, each column and each
3x3 block contains all the numbers from 1 to 9.

1	8			2			7	9
	3			1			4	
		9	7		6	3		
7	2		5		9		6	1
		5	4		1	7		
4	1		2		7		3	5
		1	6		5	8		
	6			7			5	
8	5			4			9	7

"Learn to enjoy every minute of your life. Be
happy now. Don't wait for something outside of
yourself to make you happy in the future. Think
how really precious is the time you have to
spend, whether it's at work or with your family.
Every minute should be enjoyed and savored."

Earl Nightingale

First solve the clues. All of the solutions end with the letter in the middle of the circle, and in every word an additional letter is in place. When the puzzle is complete, reading clockwise around the shaded ring of letters will reveal a word appropriate to the theme of this book.

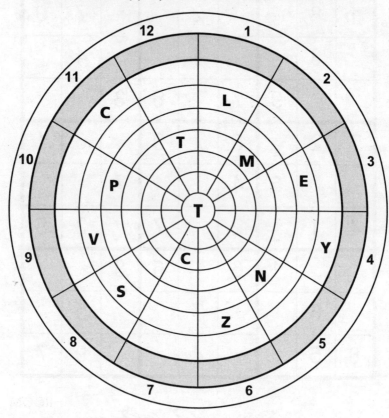

1 Forgiving under provocation

2 Item used as a decoration

3 Largest of its kind

4 Vision

5 Most slender

6 Filbert

7 Precisely and clearly expressed

8 Someone who lives at a particular place

9 Writer of story books

10 Indian or African animal

11 Austrian composer of the *Trout Quintet*

12 Less lengthy route to a destination

Answer: _____

Can you find all of the listed words hidden in the grid?
They may run forward or backward, in either a
horizontal, vertical or diagonal direction.

```
W O L L I W C G U K M B Q B B
E E R T K A O R E C Q L M E S
I R R I J S E R K O I O E N S
H O U W S P K Q C L T T O G D
R B I T E S N O O M L R I Y O
Y L R E M H O O W E B W U P E
M A R D C W H I P H T I C N E
U C W E L V I M A P L E R R K
S K E E I B X F R J G M O C Q
H B F V L H C R S A K M V R H
R E Y E S D E C L E A R I N G
O R L H N E I K E C V J U C Z
O R L Q D C O R Y S C A D E Z
M Y O Q H L E S B N S Y E I X
G H H S W K M A E R T S B L J
```

BEECH	CROW	MUSHROOM
BEETLE	DEER	OAK TREE
BIRCH	FENCE	OWL
BLACKBERRY	HEMLOCK	STREAM
BRIDLEWAY	HOLLY	SYCAMORE
CLEARING	IVY	TRUNK
COW PARSLEY	LEAVES	TWIGS
CREEPER	MAPLE	WILLOW

Criss Cross: CALM DOWN

The words are provided, but can you fit them all in the grid?

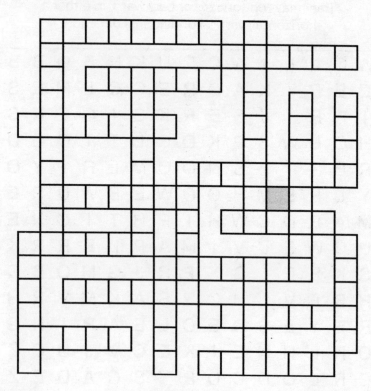

4 letters	**6 letters**	**8 letters**
HUSH	DEFUSE	CHILL OUT
	REDUCE	DECREASE
5 letters	REPOSE	DIMINISH
ABATE	SEDATE	MITIGATE
ALLAY	SETTLE	
LOWER	STEADY	**9 letters**
RELAX	TEMPER	RECONCILE
STILL		
	7 letters	**10 letters**
	APPEASE	CONCILIATE
	ASSUAGE	
	PLACATE	
	SILENCE	

One of these ice cream treats is different from
the rest. Can you spot the odd one out?

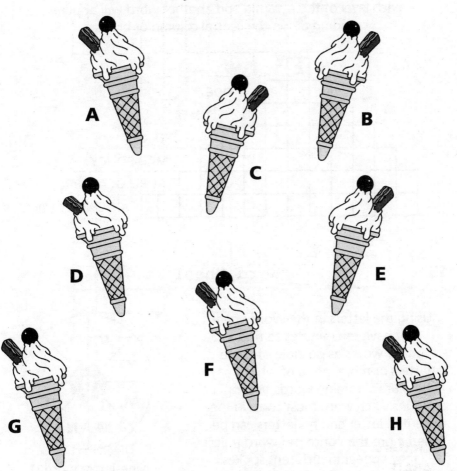

"The best and most beautiful things in
the world cannot be seen or even touched
— they must be felt with the heart."

Helen Keller

12   Pyragram

Every clue in this puzzle is an anagram leading to a single-word solution. Correctly solve the anagram on each level of the pyramid and another word will appear, reading down the central column of bricks.

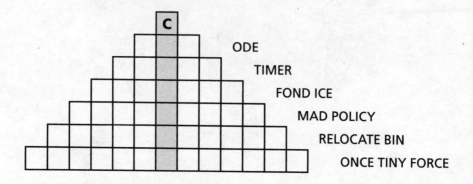

ODE

TIMER

FOND ICE

MAD POLICY

RELOCATE BIN

ONCE TINY FORCE

13   Word Wheel

Using the letters in the Wordwheel, you have ten minutes to find as many words as possible of three letters or more, none of which may be plurals, foreign words or proper nouns. Each word must contain the central letter and no letters can be used more than once per word unless they appear in different spokes of the wheel. There is at least one nine-letter word to be found.

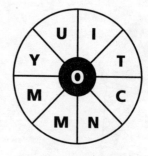

Nine-letter word(s):

_____

"Joy in looking and comprehending is nature's most beautiful gift."

Albert Einstein

Can you find all of the listed words hidden in the grid?
They may run forward or backward, in either a
horizontal, vertical or diagonal direction.

```
Z T L A W I P F A L E E R M O
T T N F L O B W L B O L E R O
E L L I R D A U Q A M A M B O
A T M K M U L G N G M U L V J
A B A P K D G U N N H E R A B
O G V O B W Y B D O Y O N J O
V Z E M G P I R D G C H X C P
D G P J R J P E Y G A C O Q O
T S I W T F S T A Y X K V P I
M V P U I A T T E C A B M A S
E Q N I K F E I W U B P A I G
S V R L M L K J K X N C M I P
N J O M E U A L X Z D I J G M
C P H V N F H N T H S V M C Y
R O G N A T S H I M M Y X V N
```

BOLERO	JITTERBUG	RUMBA
BOP	JIVE	SAMBA
BUNNY HOP	LIMBO	SHAKE
CONGA	MAMBO	SHIMMY
FLAMENCO	MINUET	TANGO
FRUG	POLKA	TWIST
HORNPIPE	QUADRILLE	VELETA
JIG	REEL	WALTZ

Enter the answer to each clue, one letter per square, in the direction indicated by the arrows. When completed, rearrange the letters in the shaded squares to spell out a word appropriate to the theme of this book.

Size of paper / Spanish sport	▼	In accompaniment or as a companion	▼	Salty Greek cheese	▼	Cone-bearing tree	▼	External forms
⌐				▼				
Chief impact of a specified action		Throughout a period of time, poetically	►			Remain, sit tight		Pretentious
⌐				Health resort near a spring / Highway	► ▼		▼	▼
Decorative tie		Stocking support / Ballroom dance	►		▼			
⌐		▼	Small case into which an object fits	Hop-drying building / Make unhappy	►			
Narrative poem of popular origin	Put to the test	►	▼	▼			One who looks after a sick relative	
⌐						Ooze	▼	Cautious
Slept lightly	Diminutive of Edward / Lubricate	►			Watched	► ▼		▼
⌐	▼				Epoch	►		
Foreign		Decorative layer	►					
⌐				Enquire in a meddlesome way	►			

Ladle the letters from the soup tureen and fit one into each of the 26 bowls on the table below, so that the finished result is a complete crossword containing English words. All of the letters in the tureen must be used – thus no letter is used more than once. When rearranged, the letters in the filled bowls spell out a variety of pea.

A B C D E F G H I J K
L M N O P Q R S
T U V W X Y Z

"Nothing is more beautiful than the loveliness of the woods before sunrise."

George Washington Carver

Which four shapes (two black
and two white) can be fitted
together to form the dolphin
shown here? The pieces may be
rotated, but not flipped over.

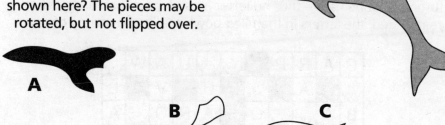

E

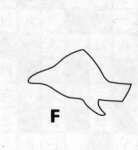

B

C

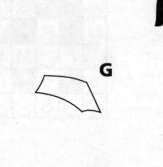

D

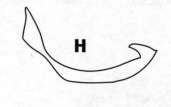

F

G

H

I

"The time you enjoy wasting
is not wasted time."

John Lennon

J

Wordsearch:
RELIGION AND RELIGIOUS FESTIVALS

Can you find all of the listed words hidden in the grid?
They may run forward or backward, in either a
horizontal, vertical or diagonal direction.

```
W L J A I L R N O I A E H H J
Y A D N U S Y T I N I R T H H
K T Y G Z L I H M H H P C Z S
J A A V A M G L Y R Q O T A N
Q D S M L A V D A Q F A L M Z
I V M E M R R S F W O Q P I M
Z A N O W J A X V I I F I V J
S T L D R B M M S I A D U J I
R E D E S M J M A K S J A N H
K T L S R A O M T D Q H A C D
Z H F O I X L N A T A G J Y O
I T E N B A H A I L A N U X B
S E I D L O B L L R S L V G D
Z S P M A E N R I U E I H H R
M T N A T S E T O R P U R I M
```

BAHA'I	LAMMAS	SADEH
BODHI	LENT	SEDER
DIWALI	MAGHI	TAOISM
HAJJ	MORMON	TIRAGAN
HOLI	OBON	TRINITY SUNDAY
ISLAM	PROTESTANT	UGADI
JAINISM	PURIM	WESAK
JUDAISM	RAMADAN	YULE

The words are provided, but can you fit them all in the grid?

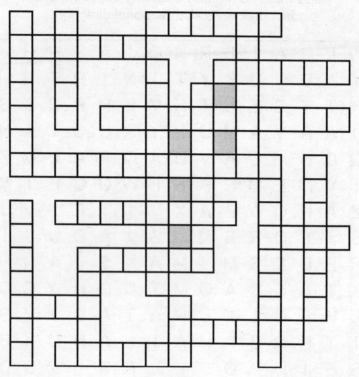

3 letters
SAY

4 letters
AVER
AVOW

5 letters
AGREE
STATE

6 letters
ALLEGE
ATTEST
DEPOSE
RATIFY
UPHOLD
VERIFY

7 letters
DECLARE
ENDORSE
PROFESS
SUPPORT

8 letters
MAINTAIN
POSITIVE

9 letters
ESTABLISH

10 letters
STRENGTHEN

11 letters
CORROBORATE

12 letters
SUBSTANTIATE

Place one of the numbers from 1 to 9 into every
empty cell so that each row, each column and each
3x3 block contains all the numbers from 1 to 9.

	2		7			1	5	
		9	2	6			7	3
1		3	5					
	6				9	4		8
5			1		7			9
8		1	4				3	
					4	9		6
2	8			3	5	7		
	4	7			2		8	

"Perfect happiness is a beautiful sunset, the
giggle of a grandchild, the first snowfall. It's
the little things that make happy moments, not
the grand events. Joy comes in sips, not gulps."

Sharon Draper

Discover a path to the image in the middle of this
maze. Start at the entrance at the top.

"The happiness of your life depends upon
the quality of your thoughts: therefore,
guard accordingly, and take care that
you entertain no notions unsuitable
to virtue and reasonable nature."

Marcus Aurelius

Can you find all of the listed words hidden in the grid?
They may run forward or backward, in either a
horizontal, vertical or diagonal direction.

```
X Z Y U C J H G A Z E E K L D
D M I B G D D G U S G O D G A
J T R E L L T U N F C R L L L
T H N N A P A R I A C P X A F
Q N G D Y F O R L R L D F N K
E I Y I Y G C O E N N S G C T
D R Y R S T U R T S H R Q E N
I G O E O W A V E S I E R W K
M F T W K Y N H O M L W O C S
V S R O B Q R Q A E S R Q H U
S D H C T A R C S C F M T S T
C Y I A Z N E L V A T N I O P
B B A L K E P O M P O F A L C
X M R W G E S T I C U L A T E
A Y J G N N F X N Z F D X E X
```

BEND	GLARE	SCRATCH
COWER	GRIMACE	SHAKE
CRINGE	GRIN	SIGH
CRY	LAUGH	SMILE
FROWN	MOPE	STOOP
GAZE	PACE	STRUT
GESTICULATE	POINT	WAVE
GLANCE	SCOWL	YAWN

The words are provided, but can you fit them all in the grid?

3 letters
MAY

4 letters
BUDS
EGGS
LENT
LILY

5 letters
BUNNY
FRESH
GREEN
GUSTY

LAMBS
MARCH
NESTS

6 letters
CALVES
GROWTH
SHOOTS
SPRING
TULIPS

7 letters
ANEMONE
PUDDLES
RAINBOW
SHOWERS

8 letters
SNOWDROP

9 letters
NARCISSUS

13 letters
MORRIS DANCERS

Place all twelve of the pieces into the grid. Any may be rotated or flipped over, but none may touch another, not even diagonally.

The numbers outside the grid refer to the number of consecutive black squares; and each block is separated from the others by at least one white square. For instance, '3 2' could refer to a row with none, one or more white squares, then three black squares, then at least one white square, then two more black squares, followed by any number of white squares.

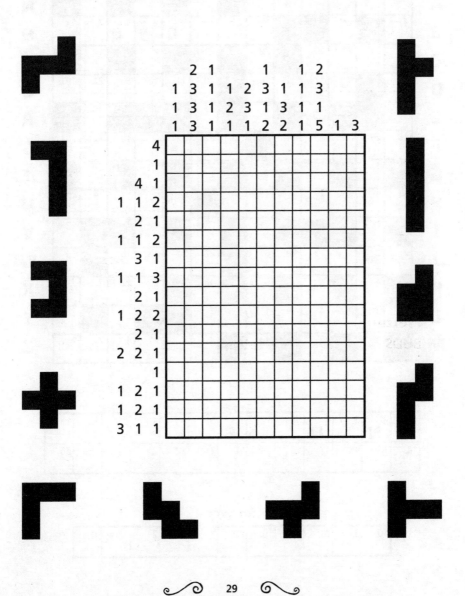

Codeword

Every letter in this crossword has been replaced by a number, the number remaining the same for that letter wherever it occurs. Can you substitute numbers for letters and complete the crossword?

Some letters have already been entered into the grid, to help you on your way. When finished, use the code to spell out the name of a butterfly.

Grid (rows A–M, left labels; right labels spell the alphabet N–Z):

A	21	14	15	11	2	1		7		10		4			N
B	4		24			19	21	9	7 (E)	2 (N)	4 (D)	7	17		O
C	8	21	25	16		22		21		21		14			P
D	12		2	12	25	16		10	11	1	2	21	19		Q
E	10			14		7		11				4			R
F	18	21	14	23	24		16	22	12	5	12	7	18		S
G		13		19		18		2		12		2			T
H	21	13	13	7	21	17	10		4	21	17	18	10		U
I		7				21		2		17			22		V
J	7	2	1	12	19	6		22	21	18	15		19		W
K		4		2		6		18		20	22	2	7		X
L	3	11	19	4	19	11	6	7			22		25		Y
M		26		22		14		4	7	21	4	7	2		Z

Code key:

1	2 (N)	3	4 (D)	5	6	7 (E)	8	9	10	11	12	13
14	15	16	17	18	19	20	21	22	23	24	25	26

Answer

10	3	21	19	19	22	3	18	21	11	19

Can you find all of the listed words hidden in the grid?
They may run forward or backward, in either a
horizontal, vertical or diagonal direction.

```
D E N R A E L S U O R O G I V
R C S G A Z R N O Y N A C E T
C D E V R E S E R I O U S A P
V I V I D P T E V P D N D R M
D I X K E Y V U A E E E O Q V
S U B G N M G S T T S F K M H
I U X A T Z S N N S O K H J G
F P O M S I K I O U A E A N G
G H N R O S E R N R A D I E N
N R Z N O R G D Q R T P S M I
I T A Y G N K P T T A S A E N
W T Y V E O O F U G O X B R W
E I D H E B E S L W R V Y T A
L S S S E L M O H T A F S X Y
A L O K T Y N T N A N O S E R
```

ABYSS	GAPING	RESONANT
ARDENT	GRAVE	SERIOUS
ASTUTE	HEARTFELT	SEVERE
BASS	INTENSE	SONOROUS
CANYON	LEARNED	STRONG
ENGROSSED	PASSIONATE	VIGOROUS
EXTREME	PROFOUND	VIVID
FATHOMLESS	RESERVED	YAWNING

The words are provided, but can you fit them all in the grid?

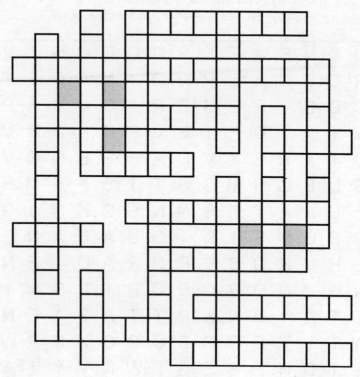

4 letters
FOOD
HOME
WORK

5 letters
SHEEP

6 letters
CLOUDS
RICHES
TRAVEL

7 letters
CASTLES
FAILURE
FALLING
FLOWERS
THE WIFE

8 letters
FLOATING
FOOTBALL
HOLIDAYS
SWIMMING

9 letters
PROMOTION
THE FUTURE

11 letters
GETTING LOST

14 letters
BECOMING
FAMOUS

First solve the clues. All of the solutions end with the letter in the middle of the circle, and in every word an additional letter is in place. When the puzzle is complete, reading clockwise around the shaded ring of letters will reveal the names of two birds.

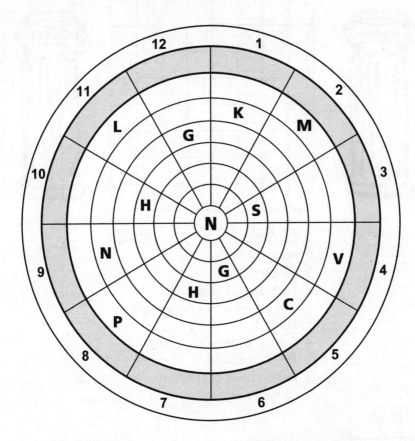

1 Country, capital Islamabad
2 Jail
3 Male child of one's child
4 Action by a landlord that compels a tenant to leave the premises
5 Event
6 Gas that forms approximately 78% of Earth's atmosphere
7 Last name of brothers George and Ira, of musical fame
8 Worker who makes glasses for remedying defects of vision
9 Charitable gift
10 Security guard
11 Conjuring trick
12 Metallic element used to make light-bulb filaments

Answer: _____ **and** _____

Place the answers in order across the horizontal rows. When completed correctly, reading down each of the shaded columns will reveal the name of a plant.

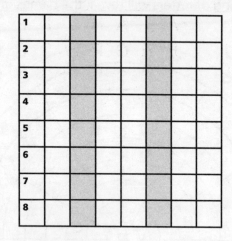

1 Collarbone
2 Put up with
3 Amulet, charm
4 Shiitake, for example
5 Government representative abroad
6 Former British coin worth five new pence
7 Patron saint of children
8 Unnecessary

"Be happy with what you have and what you are, be generous with both, and you won't have to hunt for happiness."

William E. Gladstone

Can you find all of the listed words hidden in the grid?
They may run forward or backward, in either a
horizontal, vertical or diagonal direction.

```
C H G I S A I A H Y L E T M J
A E T N L B R G P W S S G O X
L U N I D S U S E J G Z H O R
V S G E M I H D N A G N F M C
I E R M M S G L D N T A M M L
N B A O Z Q O P O H U F A U M
L I H H X Y E H E I A H A Z G
G U A K O N R B O M A P O T W
X S M L O E A U W R T R E O P
Q J A S H P S E B S O I L A W
X O N K T M M A G A V S R L A
Y M H I O Z U K S Q E H W U O
C L S S O W S T K Y A S F W R
V T E L B L E Q N M O Z J V F
A S E W X R U S S E L L M S M
```

ABRAHAM	GRAHAM	MOSES
BOOTH	ISAIAH	PARHAM
BUDDHA	JESUS	RUSSELL
CALVIN	JOHN THE BAPTIST	SEABURY
ERASMUS	KHOMEINI	SMITH
EUSEBIUS	KNOX	ST PAUL
FOX	LAO-TZU	WOLSEY
GANDHI	LOYOLA	ZOROASTER

Criss Cross: LAKES

The words are provided, but can you fit them all in the grid?

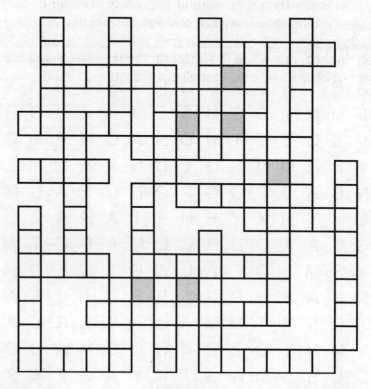

4 letters
CHAD
COMO
EYRE
KIVU

5 letters
GATUN
GLASS
HURON
NEAGH
OHRID
PATOS
RWERU
VOLTA

6 letters
EDWARD
GEORGE
IZABAL
LADOGA
LUGANO
MALAWI
POWELL

7 letters
ONTARIO
ST CLAIR
TURKANA

8 letters
MANITOBA
TIBERIUS
WINNIPEG

9 letters
GREAT SALT
NICARAGUA

Straightforward clues are presented with the crossword grid but the clues are in alphabetical order and the grid is minus its black squares. You need to black out some of the squares, resulting in a filled symmetrical crossword, as well as fill in the missing letters. When finished, rearrange the letters in the shaded squares (which must not be blacked out) to spell out the name of a wild flower.

Adolescent

Area set back or indented

Become worse or disintegrate

Bottomless gulf or pit

Capital of Canada

Creative person

Even-tempered

Expert who studies data

Expresses in speech

Feed as in a meadow or pasture

Function

Inventories

Light automatic rifle

D	E	S	I	G	N	S	P		A	C	I	D
E	V	Y	O	N	D	D	E	A	S	A	M	E
P		R	P	O	S	E	D	S	C	R	A	M
U	F	U	L	C	E	T	A	S	O		O	A
T	O	P	I	C	L	E	M	O	T	I	O	N
Y	A	C	H	H	E	R	A	G	E	N	E	D
A	F	A	C	I		I	T	A	T	E	D	S
O	W	N	E	R	S	O	R	U	M	E	N	U
T	R	A	I		E	R	E	S	I	G	H	T
T	E	L	A	I	R	A	N	T	E	R	O	T
A		Y	S	S	I	T	E	E	N	A	G	
W	A	S	S	T	Y		A	R	O	Z	E	R
A	R	T	I	S	T	D	R	E	C	E	S	S

Made easy

Make a forceful request

Noosed rope

Preliminary sketch

Scarper

Second-in-command

Severely simple

Shaped and stuffed pasta dumplings

Short preview of a film or TV programme

Strong feeling

Subject matter of a conversation

Sweet sticky liquid

The faculty of vision

Flower Power

Fit the listed words into the grid below (one letter is already in place), then rearrange the letters in the shaded squares to form the name of a flower.

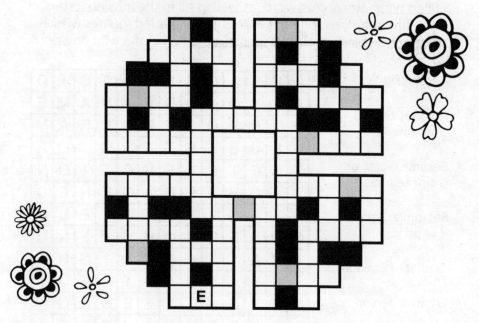

3 letters	4 letters		5 letters	
AGO	ABUT	KNOT	AMAZE	LIMBO
BUT	AURA	LASS	CLERK	LUSTY
DUO	BAKE	MAUL	FLASK	RANCH
HID	BLED	ODDS	FROTH	SHARK
KEG	DANK	RAKE	KHAKI	THIEF
NIL	GOOD	TAXI	LATIN	TOPIC
OAF				
TEN				

"We usually find that it is the simplest things – not the greatest occasions – that in retrospect give off the greatest glow of happiness."

Bob Hope

Can you find all of the listed words hidden in the grid?
They may run forward or backward, in either a
horizontal, vertical or diagonal direction.

```
U N U V O Z T F U N R N X B O
S R A J N F X O I G A S X V Z
Z A Y I O A H E S M Z Y N B N
H G B R C Z I C G A I X A P A
E T I A M I S R Z Y V F E M I
C J C S E H N E Y N P J A T S
C N C G A A E E D S L T N R R
I A D Z M H N O O E S N I S E
R F T O C O G C P H M A M A P
F E T O E F E F E V P E F N N
C T M H Y L N A B A T A E A N
O E T I T T I H Z G E M I O Y
I W H S X L Y D I A N A S N Z
G N A H S E H N A M O R A I O
Y G Y N A I N O D E L A C M H
```

ARAMAEAN	JIROFT	OTTOMAN
ASSYRIAN	LYDIAN	PERSIAN
AZTEC	MAYAN	PHOENICIAN
CALEDONIAN	MEDES	ROMAN
CELTS	MINAEAN	SABAEAN
EGYPTIAN	MINOAN	SHANG
HITTITE	MOCHE	XIA
INCA	NABATAEAN	ZHOU

The words are provided, but can you fit them all in the grid?

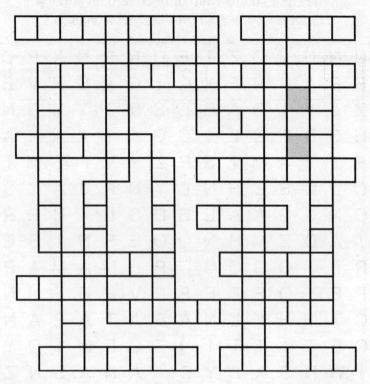

4 letters
FEAR
LOVE

5 letters
ANGER
DREAD
GUILT
PANIC
PEACE
PRIDE

6 letters
REGRET
SORROW
TERROR

7 letters
ANXIETY
BOREDOM
ECSTASY
ELATION
REMORSE

8 letters
DEVOTION

9 letters
REVERENCE
SUFFERING

10 letters
JOYFULNESS

11 letters
NERVOUSNESS

14 letters
DISAPPOINTMENT

Place one of the numbers from 1 to 9 into every empty cell so that each row, each column and each 3x3 block contains all the numbers from 1 to 9.

		1		2		5		
9	4		5		3		2	6
	2		9		7		4	
		3	8	6	9	2		
2	6						8	7
		9	2	7	4	3		
	1		6		2		7	
3	9		7		8		1	5
		7		9		4		

"Most people don't allow
the happy moment, because
they're so busy trying
to get a happy life."

Esther Hicks

Place the listed words horizontally into the grid, so that when read from top left to bottom right, the letters in the shaded squares spell out the name of a spice. Some letters are already in place.

ALKANET

BUGBANE

CATMINT

FLYTRAP

LUCERNE

NIGELLA

SAFFRON

		T				
				R		
		G				
				R		

"Courtesies of a small and trivial character are the ones which strike deepest in the grateful and appreciating heart."

Henry Clay

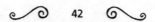

Can you find all of the listed words hidden in the grid?
They may run forward or backward, in either a
horizontal, vertical or diagonal direction.

```
D K A T L P M L R U G U G D X
R P Y E E I E I G N N D D X J
I B Q L H A A T F O T W N F C
B P P Y G R R T R O O S T E R
E N K L Y W O L N E I S N X J
T V E E S H Q E J I L P E B V
A W O F X M E B N F P I P I T
G H U D B X X U I V D F J Q F
I S T O R K T N Y X E E A Z W
R E I N G H C T B E N G U L L
F J P S A H K I T E K I R H S
W V H T K W U N X I R R B E F
M Y C V C I S G A O X P U O T
T H R U S H N N O E G I P T R
Y D H U R X H K P X N X J O R
```

DOVE	LITTLE BUNTING	ROOK
EAGLE	NUTHATCH	ROOSTER
EGRET	PETREL	SHRIKE
FINCH	PIGEON	SISKIN
FRIGATE BIRD	PINTAIL	STORK
GOOSE	PIPIT	SWAN
GULL	RHEA	THRUSH
KITE	ROBIN	TURKEY

Criss Cross:
NOBEL PEACE PRIZE WINNERS

The words are provided, but can you fit them all in the grid?

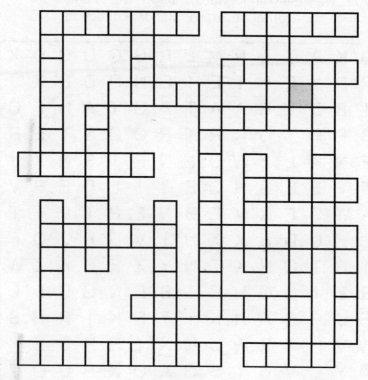

4 letters
HUME
TUTU

5 letters
ANNAN
EBADI
OBAMA
PERES
RABIN
SADAT

6 letters
ADDAMS
BRANDT
BUNCHE
CARTER
CASSIN
WALESA

7 letters
DAE-JUNG
KELLOGG
MAATHAI
MANDELA
TRIMBLE

8 letters
CORRIGAN
MARSHALL

9 letters
KISSINGER

10 letters
SCHWEITZER

Discover a path to the image in the middle of this maze. Start at the entrance at the top.

"The moments of happiness we enjoy take us by surprise. It is not that we seize them, but that they seize us."

Ashley Montagu

Place all twelve of the pieces into the grid. Any may be rotated or flipped over, but none may touch another, not even diagonally.

The numbers outside the grid refer to the number of consecutive black squares; and each block is separated from the others by at least one white square. For instance, '3 2' could refer to a row with none, one or more white squares, then three black squares, then at least one white square, then two more black squares, followed by any number of white squares.

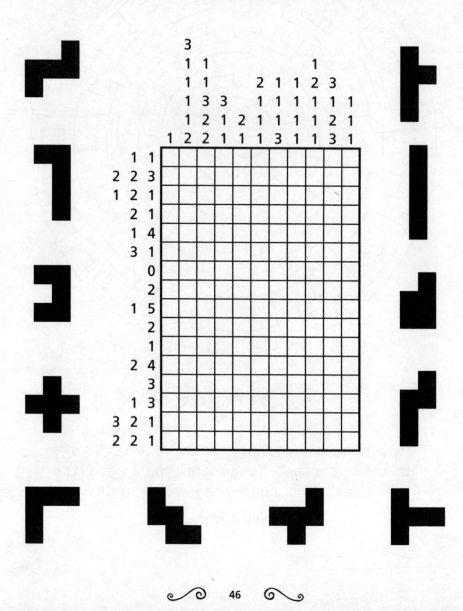

Can you find all of the listed words hidden in the grid?
They may run forward or backward, in either a
horizontal, vertical or diagonal direction.

```
C  J  B  I  B  R  E  V  A  P  A  P  N  R  N
A  C  C  H  J  W  Y  E  I  S  A  L  V  I  A
L  H  A  S  H  A  S  Q  S  O  V  T  A  G  Y
I  Z  P  N  Q  H  I  G  I  N  L  S  J  S  A
L  R  T  O  T  P  A  N  R  L  T  E  N  F  N
H  S  F  W  P  E  D  Y  I  E  S  A  T  V  T
F  S  I  D  J  P  R  L  R  X  T  J  I  V  I
R  J  R  R  B  H  Y  B  A  S  O  U  A  E  R
P  A  H  O  X  L  I  P  U  F  C  L  X  R  R
N  P  T  P  N  O  G  L  X  R  K  S  G  B  H
W  O  I  O  A  X  U  G  Y  P  Y  C  G  E  I
X  N  D  Y  A  M  E  E  I  Y  M  B  J  N  N
K  I  O  W  I  S  M  L  H  N  E  G  E  A  U
C  C  V  M  U  R  U  W  M  P  G  A  H  L  M
M  A  G  E  N  T  I  A  N  R  Q  D  L  P  L
```

ANTIRRHINUM	LILAC	SALVIA
ASTER	LILY	SNOWDROP
CANTERBURY BELL	MIMULUS	STOCK
DAISY	OXLIP	TANSY
GENTIAN	PAPAVER	THRIFT
GLOXINIA	PHLOX	TULIP
IRIS	PINK	VERBENA
JAPONICA	POPPY	VIOLET

Criss Cross: PERFUME

The words are provided, but can you fit them all in the grid?

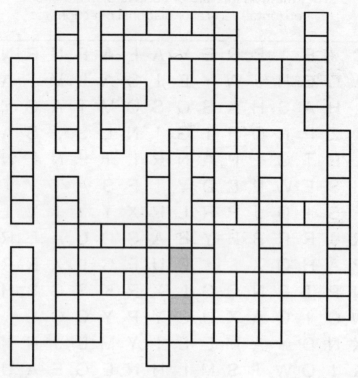

4 letters
MUSK

5 letters
AROMA
ROSES
SCENT

6 letters
CITRUS
FLORAL
FRUITY
LILIES
ORCHID
SPICES

7 letters
BOUQUET
COLOGNE
INCENSE
OAKMOSS
VIOLETS

8 letters
LAVENDER

9 letters
ORRIS ROOT
REDOLENCE
SWEETNESS

13 letters
EAU-DE-TOILETTE

One of these fruity desserts is different from the rest. Can you spot the odd one out?

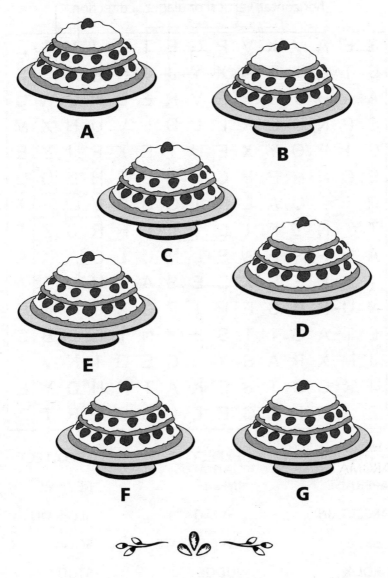

A

B

C

D

E

F

G

"Laughter is an instant vacation."
Milton Berle

Can you find all of the listed words hidden in the grid?
They may run forward or backward, in either a
horizontal, vertical or diagonal direction.

```
S E A V X V P G E T J J V C E
D T A T B D X Y J G D K I E S
A A U J E B E V R E D N O W U
S P N D O R L L D L V U H X M
C I P O Y X E U I E X F J Y E
E C H R P E C V N B S H E D D
R I I Q A E N T O B E V O V I
T T N Z F I E I L L R R S Z T
A N F S E W S L M U L O A K A
I A E F S X E E S A S U O T T
N U R B S E P I F O X O M K E
E T A G I T S E V N I E L B C
J M X P A S X S C E G I K V T
J K C O T S E K A T R H D Y E
Z J N L T C E L L O C E R T Z
```

ANTICIPATE	EXPECT	RECOLLECT
APPRAISE	INFER	REVIEW
ASCERTAIN	INVENT	SLEEP ON
ASSESS	INVESTIGATE	SOLVE
BROOK	JUDGE	STUDY
DEDUCE	MEDITATE	SURVEY
DELIBERATE	MULL OVER	TAKE STOCK
EXAMINE	MUSE ·	WONDER

First solve the clues. All of the solutions end with the letter in the middle of the circle, and in every word an additional letter is in place. When the puzzle is complete, reading clockwise around the shaded ring of letters will reveal the names of two birds.

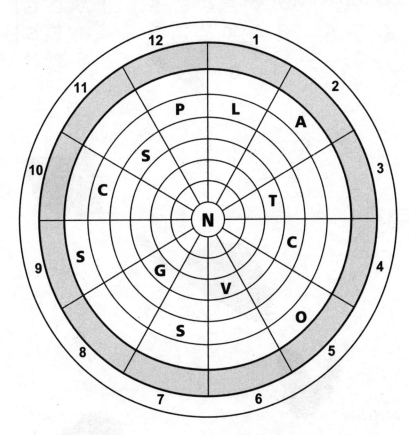

1 Male shop assistant

2 Temple to all the gods

3 Cherished desire

4 Response

5 Native of Bucharest, for example

6 State of being disregarded or forgotten

7 Receptacle for rubbish

8 Faith

9 Hired murderer

10 Holiday

11 Albert ___, physicist (1879–1955)

12 ___ Bonaparte, emperor of the French (1769–1821)

Answer: _____ **and** _____

Which four shapes (two black and two white) can be fitted together to form the tree shown here? The pieces may be rotated, but not flipped over.

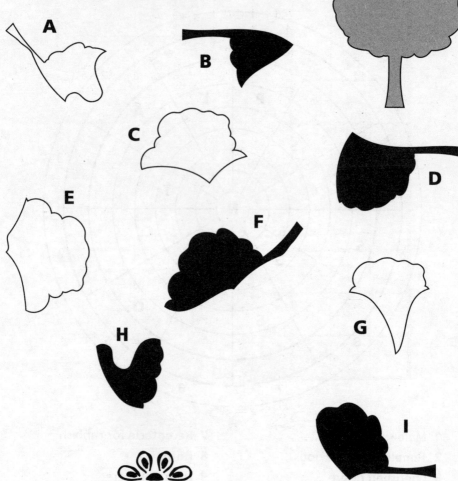

A

B

C

D

E

F

G

H

I

J

"I don't have to chase extraordinary moments to find happiness – it's right in front of me if I'm paying attention and practicing gratitude."

Brené Brown

Place one of the numbers from 1 to 9 into every empty cell so that each row, each column and each 3x3 block contains all the numbers from 1 to 9.

	9		6			7	4		
	6	1	2			5	9		
4				3				8	
1	3		4				2		
		7		2			1		
		8			9			6	5
	1			7					9
		3	5			2	7	4	
		4	1			8		5	

"Laughter is the sun that drives winter from the human face."

Victor Hugo

Can you find all of the listed words hidden in the grid?
They may run forward or backward, in either a
horizontal, vertical or diagonal direction.

```
S  S  D  L  L  F  C  H  T  D  K  W  C  T  G
T  Z  P  W  J  C  E  D  G  R  A  E  G  D  R
N  D  R  O  T  I  U  R  F  T  A  R  N  M  T
A  C  T  B  N  T  K  B  E  N  M  Y  I  R  E
R  L  F  E  Y  G  R  R  U  A  E  X  L  A  M
R  H  U  A  Q  E  E  D  E  T  E  A  L  G  P
U  B  U  T  C  N  S  R  B  R  T  S  I  U  E
C  P  P  I  A  H  C  A  O  P  N  E  F  S  R
V  K  P  N  S  P  W  X  N  I  T  E  R  W  A
P  E  S  G  X  P  S  B  S  A  R  D  N  W  T
U  S  N  P  S  I  O  I  R  U  T  E  T  B  U
O  V  E  N  C  R  A  O  R  U  O  L  F  H  R
U  X  U  I  R  R  C  O  N  E  M  I  U  P  E
K  I  N  G  R  E  D  I  E  N  T  S  N  S  M
S  G  G  E  D  V  Z  Q  K  Y  J  F  X  F  X
```

BEATING	FLOUR	SPATULA
BOWL	FRUIT	SPONGE
BUTTER	ICING	SPOON
CREAM	INGREDIENTS	SUGAR
CURRANTS	MIXER	SULTANAS
DECORATE	OVEN	TEMPERATURE
EGGS	RAISINS	TRAY
FILLING	RECIPE	WATER

The words are provided, but can you fit them all in the grid?

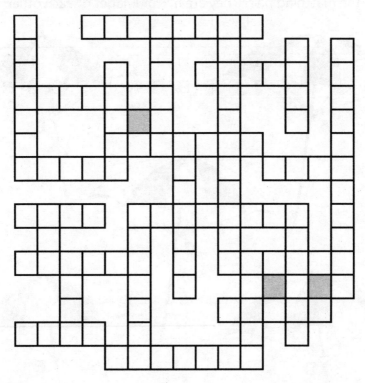

3 letters
AXE

4 letters
PEGS
RAIN
SITE
TENT
WOOD

5 letters
BEACH
GUIDE
POLES

STOVE
TORCH

6 letters
ESCAPE
FLY NET
KETTLE
STAKES

7 letters
CANTEEN
CUTLERY
GRIDDLE
HATCHET

LANTERN
OPEN AIR

8 letters
OUTDOORS
ROOF RACK

11 letters
COUNTRY CODE
GROUNDSHEET

Only two of sunshades are identical in every way. Can you spot the matching pair? They are mirror images of each other.

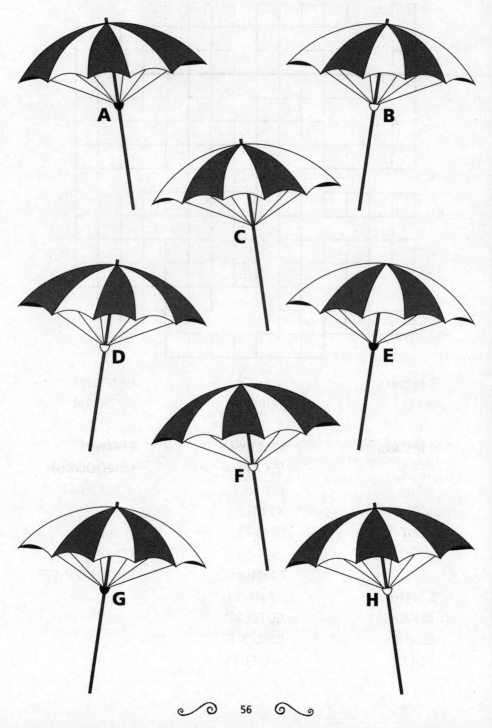

Every clue in this puzzle is an anagram leading to a single-word solution. Correctly solve the anagram on each level of the pyramid and another word will appear, reading down the central column of bricks.

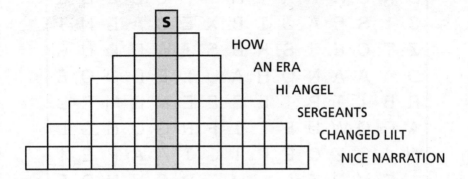

HOW

AN ERA

HI ANGEL

SERGEANTS

CHANGED LILT

NICE NARRATION

Using the letters in the Wordwheel, you have ten minutes to find as many words as possible of three letters or more, none of which may be plurals, foreign words or proper nouns. Each word must contain the central letter and no letters can be used more than once per word unless they appear in different spokes of the wheel. There is at least one nine-letter word to be found.

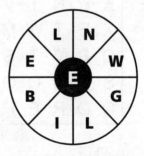

Nine-letter word(s):

_____

"If you surrendered to the air, you could ride it."

Toni Morrison

Can you find all of the listed words hidden in the grid?
They may run forward or backward, in either a
horizontal, vertical or diagonal direction.

```
D K O W F X Y H I F L B L D Q
S I S P A O T B X E C A E N T
Z T C E J S K B S I W D D U R
D A A A N O H A U L E D O O E
R B I T R I E S E E M R M R B
A P Q W U E L I F R G Q H G L
W J C Z Q E P I G T A A P E I
I G M O T L L M E H C H H R F
N B R P L L A T E T L E Z O S
G F M B L L E R U T C I P F E
K R N I V J A S U C R H C S Z
X E T W M V R G S M D A I L A
O S V T S E K T E W M O K N L
S C H O O L S V U E E F O B G
O O R E P A P R O F I L E W V
```

ASPECT	FOREGROUND	PROFILE
BATIK	FRESCO	RELIEF
CAMEO	GLAZE	SCHOOL
COLLAGE	LINES	STATUE
DRAWING	MODEL	STILL LIFE
EASEL	MURAL	TEMPERA
ETCHING	PAPER	WASH
FILBERT	PICTURE	WOODCUT

The words are provided, but can you fit them all in the grid?

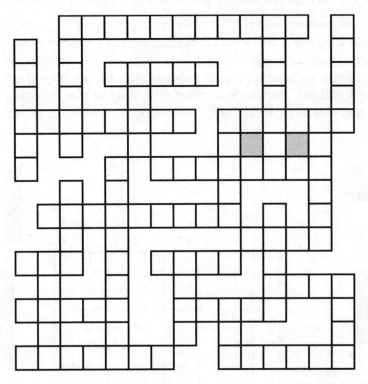

3 letters
MAY
SUN

4 letters
BUDS
EGGS
LENT
LILY
NEST
RAIN
TIDE

5 letters
APRIL
BUNNY
FRESH
GRASS
GREEN
GUSTY
MARCH

6 letters
CALVES
CROCUS
GROWTH
NATURE
TULIPS

7 letters
ANEMONE
BLOSSOM

8 letters
BLUEBELL
CLEANING

9 letters
MIGRATION
NARCISSUS

11 letters
CATERPILLAR

Place all twelve of the pieces into the grid. Any may be rotated or flipped over, but none may touch another, not even diagonally.

The numbers outside the grid refer to the number of consecutive black squares; and each block is separated from the others by at least one white square. For instance, '3 2' could refer to a row with none, one or more white squares, then three black squares, then at least one white square, then two more black squares, followed by any number of white squares.

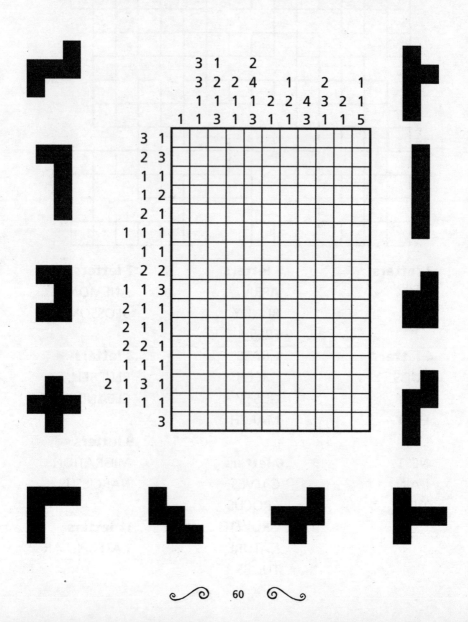

Discover a path to the image in the middle of this
maze. Start at the entrance at the top.

"The happiness of life
Is made up of minute
Fractions – the little, soon
Forgotten charities of a kiss
Or a smile, a kind look or
Heartfelt compliment."

Samuel Taylor Coleridge

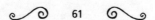

Can you find all of the listed words hidden in the grid?
They may run forward or backward, in either a
horizontal, vertical or diagonal direction.

```
G W R S K N I W Y L D D I T S
G W M S T X B D X R I U C E G
N M K R E R C A N A S T A L U
O A K G I L A T M H E V N D Y
J C R D M Q B D P E L O T A G
H H G M M W L R Z E Y U S R B
A E E S W O S K A Q G Y O C O
M C D O G R N E Y M P U L S P
A K R O T O E O V P L I I T E
I E J X M C X S P E S M T A E
K R T A E I A C T O N I A C P
I S T M C G N T H L L S I Y O
D V U I L K E O C E I Y R W O
O P M Q S K S S E I S N E S L
P J S E V I F U M S T S G J E
```

AIKIDO	DARTS	OLD MAID
ARM WRESTLING	DOMINOES	PELOTA
BO-PEEP	FIVES	POOL
BRIDGE	I SPY	ROULETTE
CANASTA	JACKS	SEVENS
CAT'S CRADLE	MAH-JONGG	SOLITAIRE
CHECKERS	MARBLES	TIC TAC TOE
CHESS	MONOPOLY	TIDDLYWINKS

The words are provided, but can you fit them all in the grid?

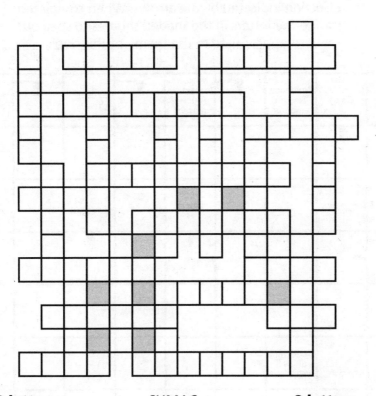

3 letters	SUMAC	**8 letters**
IVY	THUJA	ASPHODEL
	TRAYS	GLOXINIA
4 letters	VIOLA	
DILL		**9 letters**
ILEX	**6 letters**	BUTTERFLY
TAGS	ACACIA	DRAGONFLY
WREN	BARROW	FLOWERPOT
	DAHLIA	
5 letters	WEEVIL	**10 letters**
AGAVE		MARGUERITE
GORSE	**7 letters**	
LILAC	RAGWORT	
MOWER	TRELLIS	
SALIX		

Enter the answer to each clue, one letter per square, in the direction indicated by the arrows. When completed, rearrange the letters in the shaded squares to spell out a word appropriate to the theme of this book.

Pioneering motor manufacturer (5,4)	Go by	Notorious Roman emperor	▼	Minimum to maintain a nuclear reaction (8,4)	▼	Young newts	▼	Reach a destination
└▸	▼	▼			(shaded)			
Hawaiian garland of flowers	(shaded)			Unwell		That is to say (2,3)		Tea container
Aesthetic ▸				(shaded) ▼		▼		▼
▸					Egg cells ▸			
Destroy or ruin		Scratched at, as if with talons ▸						
▸				Intent	Ambit		Penetrate gradually	
Queen of the gods in Greek mythology	Tight	Finally ▸		▼	▼		▼	(shaded)
▸	▼		(shaded)			Long-tailed rodent		Bruce ___, former expert kung fu actor
Nuclear		Not concerned with right or wrong ▸				▼		▼
▸				Speed ▸		(shaded)		
Creeping or crawling invertebrates		Be in an agitated emotional state ▸						

Wordsearch: SPRING BOUQUET

Can you find all of the listed words hidden in the grid?
They may run forward or backward, in either a
horizontal, vertical or diagonal direction.

```
E S C R V A C N K F C B E D C
R N E P Q A N E M O N E L A X
L O L T I L V A S C F I L X A
L S A E H L P F O Y D I S E U
E M N L H I S L R O L U U V R
B A D O Z C T W F W C P A O I
E R I I W S D F O O Q I E L C
U A N V F D A Q R C L Q I G U
L H E O M D R C P L W R N X L
B W O C Z R X O E T A P S O A
Z T Y S N A P M P C I I B F L
F R E E S I A A S L R M T S L
N U I B L C L U U I Y L I L I
D F T O N E M T E G R O F E U
A S U E L K N I W I R E P A M
```

ALLIUM   CROCUS   MUSCARI

ANEMONE   DAFFODIL   PANSY

AURICULA   FORGET-ME-NOT   PERIWINKLE

BLUEBELL   FOXGLOVE   RAMSONS

CAMELLIA   FREESIA   SCILLA

CELANDINE   IRIS   SNOWDROP

COLTSFOOT   LILAC   TULIP

COWSLIP   LILY   VIOLET

Place one of the numbers from 1 to 9 into every empty cell so that each row, each column and each 3x3 block contains all the numbers from 1 to 9.

	4			6	2			7
		7	5			3		2
9	1				4	8		
7	6	8		4	3			
5								1
			9	8		7	3	6
		4	3				9	8
8		6			1	2		
1			2	9			5	

"The feeling that any
task is a nuisance will
soon disappear if it is
done in mindfulness."

Thich Nhat Hanh

First solve the clues. All of the solutions end with the letter in the middle of the circle, and in every word an additional letter is in place. When the puzzle is complete, reading clockwise around the shaded ring of letters will reveal a popular outdoor pastime.

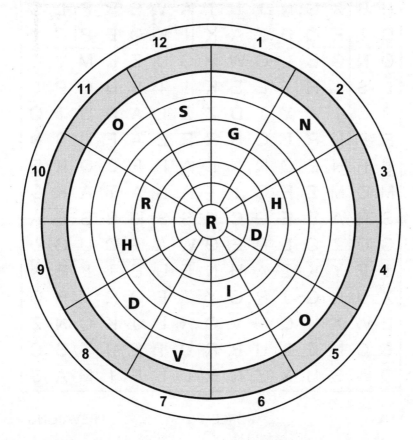

1 More lustrous

2 Designer of machinery

3 Large comfortable seat

4 Record of annual dates

5 Person who owns a guest house

6 Passageway

7 Eavesdrop

8 Person who acts as a link between parties

9 Unmarried man

10 Of the middle of a region or country

11 Month with 30 days

12 Filaments from a web spun by a spider

Answer: _____

Can you find all of the listed words hidden in the grid?
They may run forward or backward, in either a
horizontal, vertical or diagonal direction.

```
H B X G N I L I A V E R P L C
D I E Q D Z A K I K O E P C Y
O N G B L O W M G U Z K M V C
L S I H T E E K I T S U G P L
D C I W Y T D Z Z L A N U T O
R F N R L Q B R R Z A F U S N
U F N E O R X L A P F C Q K E
M O M Z E C I T A B A T A K D
S R A E E G C H S S M B B F A
G C Z C L P E O W A T O U O D
I E Y K Z A H N E U E T L E N
X U H G J R G Y T F Q R Y H O
E W X U Q M V O R L J K O N Z
E C N E L U B R U T E U T B O
Q W S U X Z N R L L E I M A S
```

BLAST	FORCE	PREVAILING
BLOW	GALE	PUFF
BOREAS	GENTLE	SAMIEL
BREEZE	GUST	SIROCCO
CALIMA	HIGH	TURBULENCE
CYCLONE	KATABATIC	WHIRLWIND
DOLDRUMS	LOMBARDE	ZEPHYR
FOEHN	MELTEMI	ZONDA

The words are provided, but can you fit them all in the grid?

3 letters	MOUSE	**8 letters**
TOM	QUEEN	FOOD BOWL
		GARFIELD
4 letters	**6 letters**	
CUTE	BASKET	**9 letters**
MANX	CATNIP	MARMALADE
PAWS	COLLAR	NINE LIVES
TAIL	GINGER	
	NEPETA	
5 letters		
CLAWS	**7 letters**	
FELIX	CATFLAP	
FLEAS	FUR BALL	
HAIRS	MOGGIES	
	SINGING	

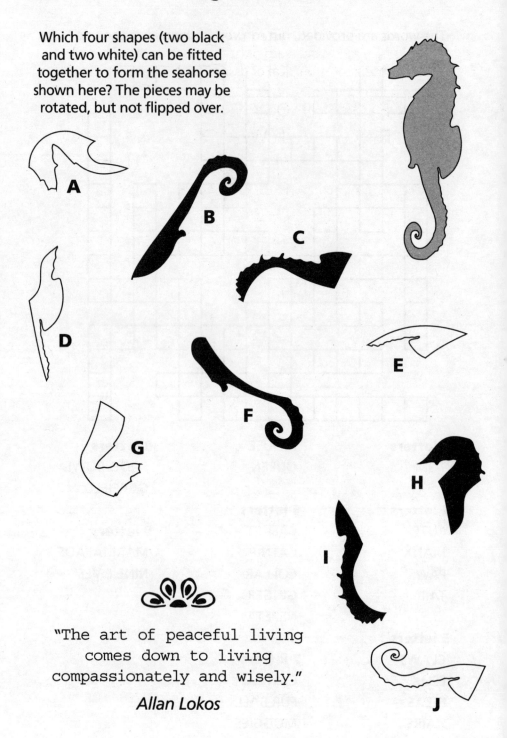

Which four shapes (two black and two white) can be fitted together to form the seahorse shown here? The pieces may be rotated, but not flipped over.

A

B

C

D

E

F

G

H

I

J

"The art of peaceful living comes down to living compassionately and wisely."

Allan Lokos

Can you find all of the listed words hidden in the grid?
They may run forward or backward, in either a
horizontal, vertical or diagonal direction.

```
A L F O R N O Y Z X E Y R A E
C P R V I V I W A D J N M T U
X A B Y J C M Q A N I E U N H
C R G Y R S P L D T R O D E N
O I E A O K U Z A I R O M L E
C S F U R O F R C C G F M B E
O I S P R N G A N M L A U A D
T E Y O O U I E O O H A H I A
T N R I A N E Q R C D Z S D N
E N F V E L T E O N F A Q U I
R E R R E Z N M E B Q I B G R
O H I E V T E X T N V P D F A
U N T L I J D A U S S O O V M
X P S N X G L N A Y Y D R R V
V G E V Y P A Y S A N N E J W
```

AL DENTE	DORE	MORNAY
AL FORNO	EN CROUTE	PARISIENNE
AMERICAINE	EN DAUBE	PAYSANNE
AU GRATIN	FARCI	ROULADE
AU POIVRE	FLORENTINE	ROUX
COCOTTE	GARNI	SAUTE
DIABLE	MARINADE	SOUSE
DOPIAZA	MOCHA	STIR-FRY

The words are provided, but can you fit them all in the grid?

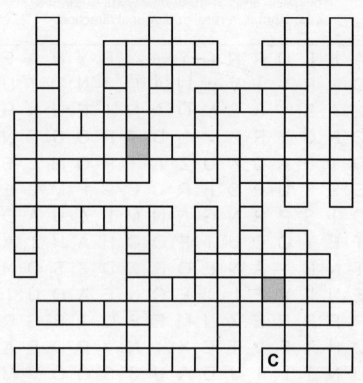

4 letters
BOWL
BUNS
CAKE
MUGS
PATE
SALT
WINE

5 letters
APPLE
CLOTH
FLASK
PLATE

SALAD
WATER

6 letters
BANANA
CHEESE
COFFEE
CRISPS
GATEAU
PEPPER
SWEETS

7 letters
CHICKEN
LETTUCE
PICKLES

8 letters
HAM ROLLS
LEMONADE

10 letters
MAYONNAISE

Discover a path to the image in the middle of this maze. Start at the entrance at the top.

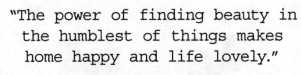

"The power of finding beauty in the humblest of things makes home happy and life lovely."

Louisa May Alcott

Place all twelve of the pieces into the grid. Any may be rotated or flipped over, but none may touch another, not even diagonally.

The numbers outside the grid refer to the number of consecutive black squares; and each block is separated from the others by at least one white square. For instance, '3 2' could refer to a row with none, one or more white squares, then three black squares, then at least one white square, then two more black squares, followed by any number of white squares.

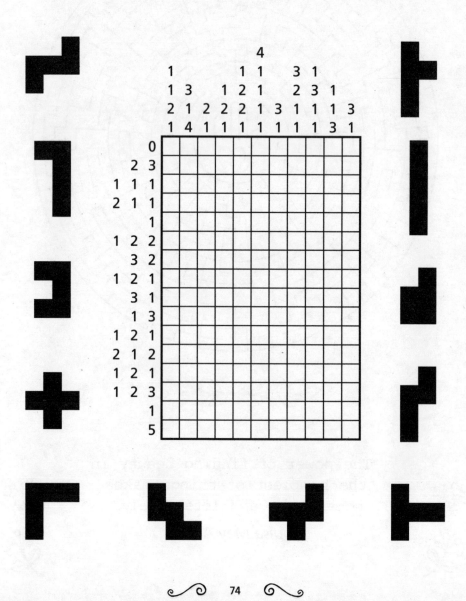

Can you find all of the listed words hidden in the grid?
They may run forward or backward, in either a
horizontal, vertical or diagonal direction.

```
E T I D O R H P A T R A G U S
O T H Q C T A Y G T E Q I H A
H W B E A U T I F U L N L C F
A Y D X M K R N E O W T D R X
J E H S I R H I V U N B I E D
I N H S U L T E E R E E A R
J T S W U U R O M I N T R F E
D I P U C R W H F D E H U A E
E E X H T D C I S O K A S I R
A T M S O A Q H T L X N A R I
N D N O T K I T T E N D E E S
G D R T T P K N T N O S R S E
E K A K W I D O G T V O T T D
L H E Y B P O M E X S M Q H U
I L Y L O V I N G A A E L Z Q
```

ANGEL	DOTE	KITTEN
APHRODITE	EMOTION	LOVER
ATTACHMENT	EROS	LOVING
BEAUTIFUL	FAIREST	SUGAR
CRUSH	FRIENDSHIP	TENDER
CUPID	HANDSOME	TREASURE
CUTIE	IDOL	TRUE
DESIRE	KISS	YEARN

Place one of the numbers from 1 to 9 into every empty cell so that each row, each column and each 3x3 block contains all the numbers from 1 to 9.

7					8			
6				2		4	8	9
1			4	3				
	6	4	8		3	1	2	
8		9				3		5
	7	1	5		2	6	9	
				5	4			1
9	5	6		7				4
			6					2

"Think big thoughts but relish small pleasures."

H. Jackson Brown, Jr.

One of these dolls is different from the rest.
Can you spot the odd one out?

Ladle the letters from the soup tureen and fit one into each of the 26 bowls on the table below, so that the finished result is a complete crossword containing English words. All of the letters in the tureen must be used – thus no letter is used more than once. When rearranged, the letters in the filled bowls spell out a variety of peach.

A B C D E F G H I J K

L M N O P Q R S

T U V W X Y Z

"I grew up around people that enjoyed life day to day and found pleasure in simple things."

Josh Turner

Can you find all of the listed words hidden in the grid?
They may run forward or backward, in either a
horizontal, vertical or diagonal direction.

```
R S P D W O L Z F H G Q K Y I
L V E T O I W I C K E R F P M
E A W G H L R P R E D L A M L
L E O P V S I W E Y S O U V E
D A J Y E E U V Q T Y S B X H
K A D M N D E T E K H D Y C O
A B L Z E K O J P D Y V R B V
I C E L O E B O N Y V A E R S
T H K N I N Y J W J L L I I P
G E T E Z D A C S E Y A W A R
H S A U L E A K H V L O C R U
P T V T N P Q N T L L P R U C
Q N X I E L A R A L P O P P E
G U P A L A A M I R A S L A B
C T Y G J L K W W P G I G K A
```

ALDER	ELM	PINE
APPLEWOOD	EUCALYPTUS	POPLAR
ASH	FIR	SPRUCE
BALSA	GRANADILLA	TEAK
BRIAR	LARCH	WALNUT
CHESTNUT	MAPLE	WICKER
DEAL	OAK	WILLOW
EBONY	OLIVE	YEW

The words are provided, but can you fit them all in the grid?

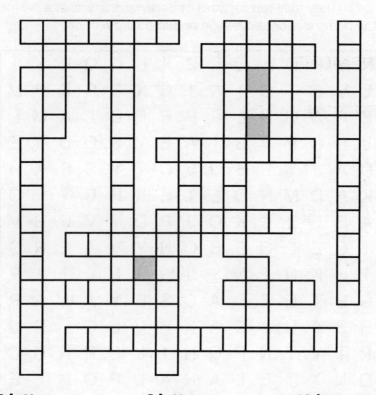

4 letters
KIWI
LIME

5 letters
HONEY
LEMON
MANGO
PEACH

6 letters
CHERRY
COFFEE
PEANUT
TOFFEE

7 letters
APRICOT
CARAMEL
PRALINE
SHERBET

10 letters
CAPPUCCINO
REDCURRANT

12 letters
CLOTTED
  CREAM
FOREST FRUITS
RUM AND
  RAISIN

Place the listed words horizontally into the grid, so that when read from top left to bottom right, the letters in the shaded squares spell out the name of a vegetable. Some letters are already in place.

ANEMONE

CHERVIL

LOBELIA

MAYWEED

MORINGA

OREGANO

RHUBARB

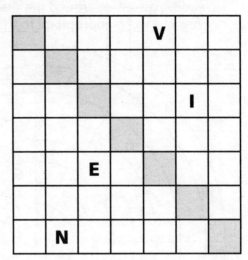

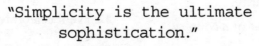

"Simplicity is the ultimate sophistication."

Leonardo da Vinci

First solve the clues. All of the solutions end with the
letter in the middle of the circle, and in every word an
additional letter is in place. When the puzzle is complete,
reading clockwise around the shaded ring of letters will
reveal a word appropriate to the theme of this book.

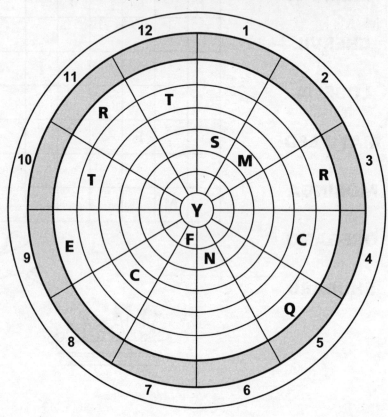

1 Lineage

2 Apothecary's shop

3 Main concern, precedence

4 Process of getting better

5 Fairness, parity

6 Legal tender of a country

7 Distinguish

8 Done in a friendly spirit

9 Characteristic likelihood of or
natural disposition toward

10 Close or warm friendship

11 Commonplace

12 Event celebrated at Christmas

Answer: _____

Can you find all of the listed words hidden in the grid?
They may run forward or backward, in either a
horizontal, vertical or diagonal direction.

```
T O R T N Z S Q T A C K I N G
M M M R N E W G J X L R R I L
O O A U C E D W N K O P F B W
F Y D Q A Z M G J L O X P B N
S S L E P T U R I P P B D O B
C M J S L A T A A N S B G B K
I R S L L L T T A G G M S L E
S O S E B E T E J T H E A C G
S F F T L E E J L O U H A N T
O S C A R V I R O D C L I Y H
R S O N B E E K W P E T Q C R
S E T Z T R S D I N T E S A E
Y R T S E W I N G U M I N M A
J D O M L K S C C E L V H Z D
D C N J Q O E R L K T D P H O
```

BOBBIN	HOOKS	SELVEDGE
CHALK	LACE	SEWING
COTTON	MODEL	SILK
CUTTING	NEEDLE	SPOOL
DRESS FORM	PATTERN	TACKING
EDGING	PINS	TAILOR
FABRIC	REELS	THREAD
GARMENT	SCISSORS	YARN

The words are provided, but can you fit them all in the grid?

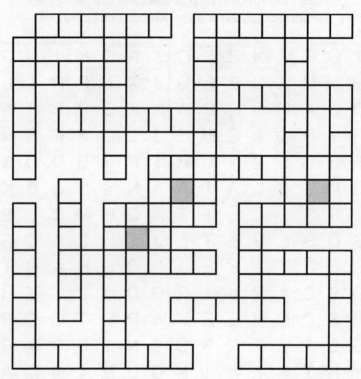

5 letters
BOATS
BRINY
INLET
POOLS
SPADE
SPRAY
TIDES
TOWEL
WAVES

6 letters
BIKINI
LIMPET
SHELLS
SUNBED

7 letters
BATHING
MUSSELS
PARASOL
PEBBLES
SANDALS
SHINGLE
SHRIMPS

8 letters
SOFT SAND

9 letters
BEACH-BALL
LIFEGUARD
PROMENADE

Fit the listed words into the grid below (one letter is already in place), then rearrange the letters in the shaded squares to form the name of a flower.

3 letters	4 letters		5 letters	
ERA	BIKE	KEEL	ADULT	NOBLE
GAP	BIND	LOST	AMPLE	NUTTY
LET	CROP	MALT	BATHE	PESTO
MOB	CUSP	PARK	ENTRY	PLANT
NAP	DAIS	RIFT	GHOUL	ROWAN
OAR	DEFY	WEST	NEWTS	SPRAY
WAR				
YET				

"A life-long blessing for children is to fill them with warm memories of times together. Happy memories become treasures in the heart to pull out on the tough days of adulthood."

Charlotte Kasl

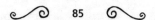

Codeword

Every letter in this crossword has been replaced by a number,
the number remaining the same for that letter wherever it occurs.
Can you substitute numbers for letters and complete the crossword?

Some letters have already been entered into the
grid, to help you on your way. When finished, use
the code to spell out the name of a butterfly.

A ... **N**
B ... **O**
C ... **P**
D ... **Q**
E ... **R**
F ... **S**
G ... **T**
H ... **U**
I ... **V**
J ... **W**
K ... **X**
L ... **Y**
M ... **Z**

A	22	23	15	7	6		10	23	6	23	9	24	19
B	19		21		21		7		23		24		14
C	19	10	19	1	23	16	20		15	8	7	14	18
D	6		1		25		26		21		1		1
E	21	23	7	16		22	23	20		3	5	1	23
F			4		17	3	12		1				11
G	7	14	4	16	24	13		2	3	10	22	7	19
H	14				18		25	7	8		1		
I	15 S	19 E	23 A	10		6	23	25		18	23	16	19
J	25		10		4		1		4		11		11
K	19	1	23	15	19		15	23	24	15	23	18	19
L	6		2		19		3		15		20		14
M	8	1	19	23	15	3	14		15	6	3	24	8

1	2	3	4	5	6	7	8	9	10	11	12	13

14	15 S	16	17	18	19 E	20	21	22	23 A	24	25	26

Answer

6	23	22	22	23	18	19		26	21	7	8	19

Can you find all of the listed words hidden in the grid?
They may run forward or backward, in either a
horizontal, vertical or diagonal direction.

```
K W H T Y R J T F I C T I O N
S B D O O D E S I O N X D L J
A V B L U E U T Q T S E A H E
H E J P Q M J T I A L T O M R
E A F C D U R L S R U E O J V
A N T H O L O G Y E W T J R N
Z X H L Y O T R I A I X H V Y
C D R Q A V I L N D Y R W O Z
C F E I X S D B A I X P E A R
U R C Y R T E O P N F G J S Q
B U I N D E X L P G R I R S M
I F P M E M F A D U N U C M G
B Z E J E K V A I K D E O S O
L Z S J S U R U A S E H T J J
E Z O C H R O N I C L E H E L
```

ANTHOLOGY	INDEX	STORY
ATLAS	JOURNAL	STUDY
AUTHOR	PLOT	TEXT
BIBLE	POETRY	THESAURUS
CHRONICLE	READING	TITLE
CRIME	RECIPES	TOME
EDITOR	SCI-FI	VOLUME
FICTION	SERIES	WRITER

The words are provided, but can you fit them all in the grid?

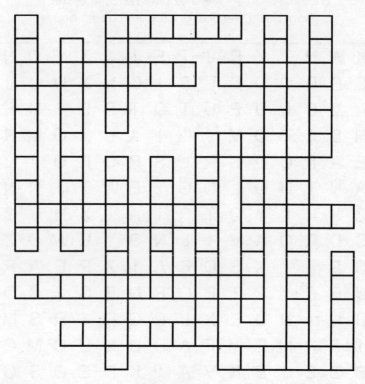

4 letters
GLAD

5 letters
JOLLY
LUCKY
MERRY
PERKY

6 letters
ELATED
JOCUND
JOVIAL
JOYFUL
LIVELY

7 letters
PLEASED

8 letters
ANIMATED
THRILLED

9 letters
EXUBERANT
FORTUNATE
FRIVOLOUS
GRATIFIED
OVERJOYED

10 letters
UNTROUBLED

11 letters
ON CLOUD NINE

Discover a path to the image in the middle of this maze. Start at the entrance at the top.

"Even though I don't have a lot of spare time, what I do have I'm very protective of, and so I make sure to have a normal life and to remember that, while it's important to keep in mind these conflicts are ongoing, it's also important to enjoy simple pleasures, too."

Clarissa Ward

Place one of the numbers from 1 to 9 into every empty cell so that each row, each column and each 3x3 block contains all the numbers from 1 to 9.

		8	3				7	6
		2		5	1	3		8
	9		8					5
6				7		8	1	
	7		6		9		4	
	3	9		4				2
1					7		3	
3		4	9	1		6		
9	5				6	2		

"Beautify your inner dialogue.
Beautify your inner world with
love, light and compassion.
Life will be beautiful."

Amit Ray

The words are provided, but can you fit them all in the grid?

4 letters
MANX
THAI

5 letters
ASIAN
KORAT
TABBY

6 letters
BIRMAN
BOMBAY
LAPERM

7 letters
BURMESE
PERSIAN

8 letters
BALINESE
BURMILLA
KARELIAN
MUNCHKIN
SIBERIAN

9 letters
PETERBALD

10 letters
ABYSSINIAN
TURKISH VAN

11 letters
EGYPTIAN MAU

Place all twelve of the pieces into the grid. Any may be rotated or flipped over, but none may touch another, not even diagonally.

The numbers outside the grid refer to the number of consecutive black squares; and each block is separated from the others by at least one white square. For instance, '3 2' could refer to a row with none, one or more white squares, then three black squares, then at least one white square, then two more black squares, followed by any number of white squares.

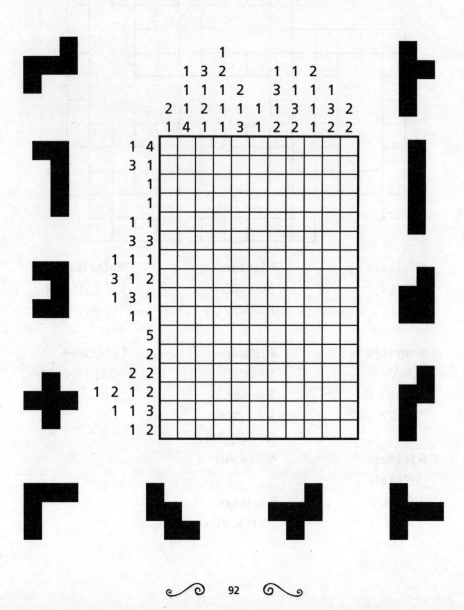

Straightforward clues are presented with the crossword grid but the clues are in alphabetical order and the grid is minus its black squares. You need to black out some of the squares, resulting in a filled symmetrical crossword, as well as fill in the missing letters. When finished, rearrange the letters in the shaded squares (which must not be blacked out) to spell out the name of a wild flower.

Brine

Showing a lack of partiality

Commenced

Cut thinly

Deliciously juicy

Detect

Elaborate cake

Exclude

Formal public statement

Geographical feature such as Krakatoa

Hostile

Increase

Mismatched

Money paid regularly for doing work

Musée du ___, principal museum and art gallery of France

Native New Zealander

Novices

Pair of parallel rails

Peculiar

Runners used for gliding over snow

Sharp-eyed birds

Squirrel's nest

Venetian canal boat

Weeps convulsively

S	O	B		T	U	N	B	I	A	S	E	D
E	W	E	U	R	R	O	U	N	D	T	L	
A	U	G	M	E	N	T	I	C	A	R	V	E
W	S	A	T	M	A	I	L	O	T	A	E	Y
A	N	N	O		N	C	E	M	E	N	T	E
T	E	N	O	N	H	E	L		E	G	E	
E		G	L	E	S	A	G	A	T	E	A	U
R	K	O	O	R	E	L	A	T	E	D	U	S
W	A	N	T	A	G	O	N	I	S	T	I	C
O	L	D	A	T	E	U	R	B	E	R	S	I
M	A	O		I	N	V	O	L	C	A	N	O
I	L	L	S	O	T	R	E	E	L	C	O	U
T	R	A	I	N	E	E	S	E	S		I	S

"Isn't it a pleasure to study and practise what you have learned?"

Confucius

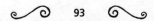

Pyragram

Every clue in this puzzle is an anagram leading to a single-word solution. Correctly solve the anagram on each level of the pyramid and another word will appear, reading down the central column of bricks.

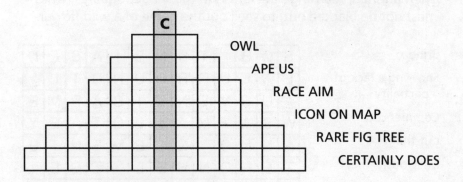

OWL

APE US

RACE AIM

ICON ON MAP

RARE FIG TREE

CERTAINLY DOES

91 Word Wheel

Using the letters in the Wordwheel, you have ten minutes to find as many words as possible of three letters or more, none of which may be plurals, foreign words or proper nouns. Each word must contain the central letter and no letters can be used more than once per word unless they appear in different spokes of the wheel. There is at least one nine-letter word to be found.

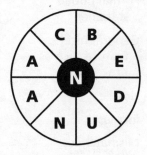

Nine-letter word(s):

_____

"Pleasure is always derived from something outside you, whereas joy arises from within."

Eckhart Tolle

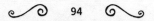

Can you find all of the listed words hidden in the grid?
They may run forward or backward, in either a
horizontal, vertical or diagonal direction.

```
V G A V W R S W A N L A K E F
T S Y K E O R M F S U N A R U
S A R K A P A K K A O U G I U
R U Z L H P M F R W A O A I O
A F N I H N I H J R I H S I E
L O E E M E U G A R P P N O M
O E S U V A Y M Z I G P E Z P
I N T S S M A R P Y S A E D E
P U P G A T Q Y F P F S O L R
A T A V A T L V N F A R E A O
T P R P T A B O R T M C I M R
I E J A Q T R D U I I Y I E L
T N O R G C A R N I V A L R Y
A G M I R I N V Y H G J B B V
N G G S E N C L X O V M H D G
```

AUTUMN	NIMROD	TAMARA
CARNIVAL	PARIS	TAPIOLA
EMPEROR	PRAGUE	TASSO
EN SAGA	SAPPHO	TITAN
LA MER	SARKA	TRAGIC
MARS	SATURN	URANUS
MESSIAH	SWAN LAKE	VENUS
NEPTUNE	TABOR	VLTAVA

Criss Cross: BIRDS

The words are provided, but can you fit them all in the grid?

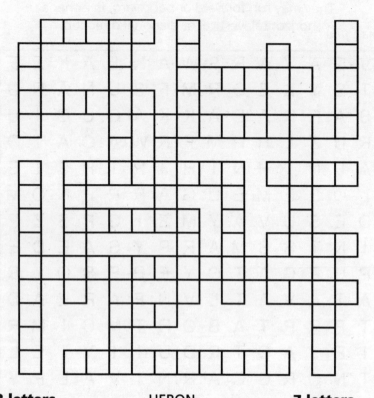

3 letters
AUK

4 letters
CROW
GULL
KITE
RHEA
ROOK
SWAN

5 letters
BOOBY
CRANE
GREBE

HERON
HOBBY

6 letters
AVOCET
BULBUL
CURLEW
DIPPER
LINNET
PLOVER
TURKEY

7 letters
BLUE TIT

8 letters
DOTTEREL

9 letters
DOWITCHER
GYRFALCON

10 letters
SHEARWATER

11 letters
TREE CREEPER

Enter the answer to each clue, one letter per square, in the direction indicated by the arrows. When completed, rearrange the letters in the shaded squares to spell out a word appropriate to the theme of this book.

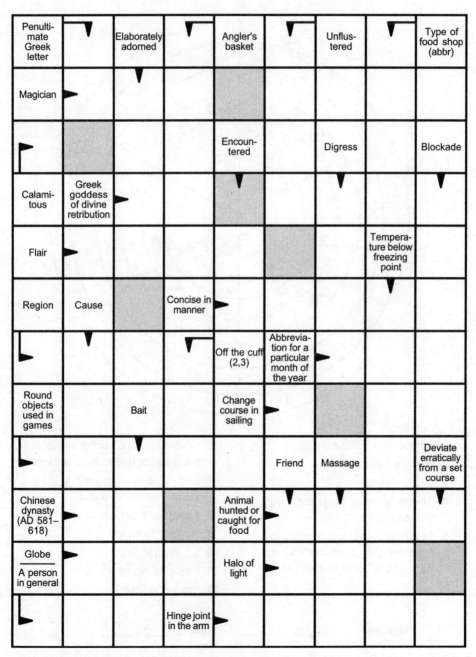

First solve the clues. All of the solutions end with the letter in the middle of the circle, and in every word an additional letter is in place. When the puzzle is complete, reading clockwise around the shaded ring of letters will reveal the names of two birds.

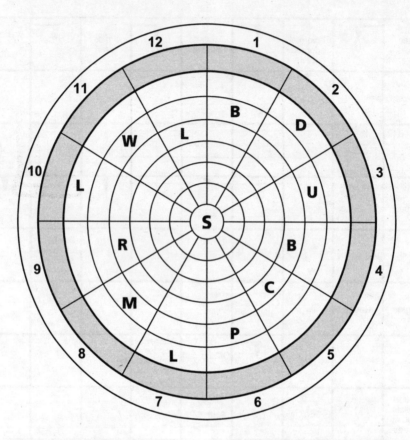

1 Legendary, extraordinary
2 State of inactivity
3 Sickening
4 Three-headed dog guarding the entrance to Hades
5 Mythological hero noted for his strength, who performed 12 tasks to gain immortality

6 Cold-blooded vertebrates such as tortoises and snakes
7 Dots in a text showing suppression of words
8 Capital of Syria
9 Armed fighters
10 US Prairie State
11 In these times
12 Young geese

Answer: _____ **and** _____

Place the answers in order across the horizontal rows. When completed correctly, reading down each of the shaded columns will reveal the name of a plant.

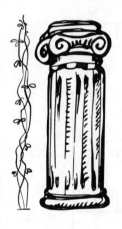

1						
2						
3						
4						
5						
6						
7						
8						

1 Unmarried man
2 Japanese word meaning 'goodbye'
3 Queen of England from 1837 to 1901
4 Spectator, observer
5 Absurd or inferior imitation
6 Folksy, as of wisdom
7 Reverse (a ruling, etc)
8 Ancient language of India

"Reason well from the beginning and then there will never be any need to look back with confusion and doubt."

Dalai Lama

The words are provided, but can you fit them all in the grid?

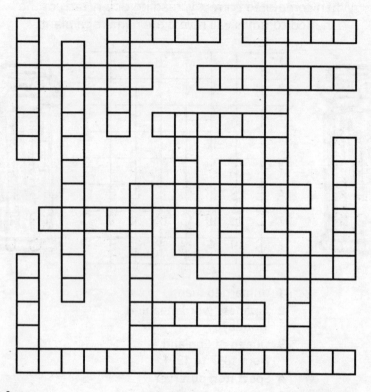

5 letters
ICING
LARDY
LAYER
MOCHA
POUND

6 letters
CARROT
CHEESE
CHERRY
DUNDEE
ECCLES
MARBLE

ORANGE
SCONES

7 letters
CURRANT
FILLING
MIXTURE

8 letters
DOUGHNUT
MACAROON
MARZIPAN

9 letters
CHRISTMAS

11 letters
LEMON SPONGE

Can you find all of the listed words hidden in the grid? They may run forward or backward, in either a horizontal, vertical or diagonal direction.

```
C D E N E P P A H X R D E M H
H C N U A L S J J T E E D G K
J E S T A B L I S H T R E C M
L X S N I D E N I M R E T E D
Q H T C G C M J M D I V A A L
D E V R E S B O E L E O I G E
C H A N C E D C R N V C T R T
L O E Q C U A U V C E E I O U
O D F U P R L D T A D R N U T
I L P U T E S Q Q M K Q I N I
I O U M D W I T N E S S E D T
A H O H T R A E N U Q D H L S
E T A N I G I R O P T S E H N
N O T I C E D O Z C S F A H I
G G A Y R E C E I V E D L W Z
```

CAME UP	INITIATED	RECOVERED
CHANCED	INSTITUTE	RETRIEVED
DETERMINED	LAUNCH	RULED
ESTABLISH	NOTICED	SAW
FELT	OBSERVED	SET UP
GOT HOLD	ORIGINATE	TRACED
GROUND	PLANT	UNEARTH
HAPPENED	RECEIVED	WITNESSED

Discover a path to the image in the middle of this maze. Start at the entrance at the top.

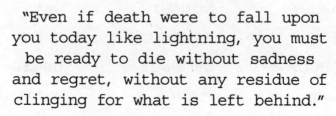

"Even if death were to fall upon you today like lightning, you must be ready to die without sadness and regret, without any residue of clinging for what is left behind."

Dilgo Khyentse Rinpoche

Place one of the numbers from 1 to 9 into every
empty cell so that each row, each column and each
3x3 block contains all the numbers from 1 to 9.

	3	2		9		1		7
			5	4	7			
		9					8	6
3	5	8	6				9	
6			7		5			2
	1				9	6	4	5
8	6					2		
			2	7	3			
7		5		6		9	1	

"It is when we ask for
love less and begin
giving it more that the
basis of human love
is revealed to us."

Leo Buscaglia

Can you find all of the listed words hidden in the grid?
They may run forward or backward, in either a
horizontal, vertical or diagonal direction.

U	P	B	H	T	W	O	R	G	G	G	R	X	P	Z
W	B	R	B	Y	A	S	V	R	S	X	Y	Y	U	V
E	O	U	B	J	M	N	E	T	T	E	Q	K	S	W
A	D	B	J	B	E	E	O	H	M	Q	M	D	S	F
S	R	K	N	Y	N	O	Y	L	U	U	M	Z	Y	Y
J	E	F	I	I	H	N	C	V	E	I	P	S	W	T
J	V	J	Q	S	A	A	E	I	S	N	H	T	I	S
M	E	S	D	P	L	R	U	O	B	O	T	L	L	U
B	F	F	R	V	D	C	L	L	W	X	A	I	L	G
O	S	I	E	A	F	I	O	E	K	M	N	D	O	L
H	L	S	N	R	L	S	R	T	B	T	E	O	W	O
U	S	T	E	Y	S	S	B	S	E	W	M	F	P	K
V	C	S	Y	O	Z	U	T	Y	G	P	O	F	S	M
W	H	A	M	N	I	S	D	Q	G	U	N	A	O	F
M	M	H	N	J	I	N	O	G	S	P	E	D	P	X

ANEMONE	FEVER	MAY
APRIL	FRESH	NARCISSUS
BLOSSOM	GREEN	PUSSY WILLOW
BUDS	GROWTH	RAINBOW
CALVES	GUSTY	SHOOTS
DAFFODIL	LAMBS	SHOWERS
EGGS	LENT	VERDANT
EQUINOX	LILY	VIOLETS

The words are provided, but can you fit them all in the grid?

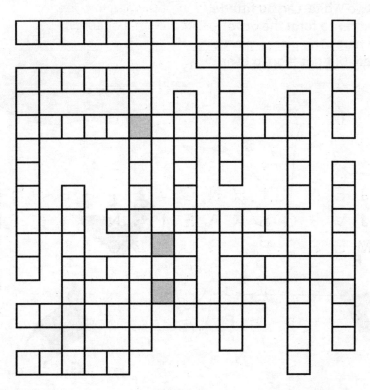

3 letters	6 letters	8 letters
PEA	CARROT	ALPHABET
	OXTAIL	BEETROOT
4 letters	POTAGE	CONSOMME
BEEF	POTATO	GAZPACHO
	TOMATO	
5 letters		**9 letters**
BROTH	**7 letters**	PEPPER POT
ONION	CHICKEN	VEGETABLE
PASTA	CHOWDER	
STOCK	WINDSOR	**10 letters**
		MINESTRONE

11 letters
COCK-A-LEEKIE

Which four shapes (two black and two white) can be fitted together to form the dove shown here? The pieces may be rotated, but not flipped over.

A

B

C

D

E

F

G

H

I

J

"Materialism is the only form of distraction from true bliss."

Douglas Horton

Can you find all of the listed words hidden in the grid?
They may run forward or backward, in either a
horizontal, vertical or diagonal direction.

```
I  P  E  A  C  E  Y  K  O  C  S  A  B  A  T
J  D  S  Z  M  P  R  I  C  E  L  E  S  S  S
A  S  O  W  Y  E  I  N  T  L  U  X  O  R  E
C  E  R  L  J  Q  A  A  B  M  A  S  O  I  R
K  Y  Y  N  E  B  F  S  Q  M  A  R  H  S  A
W  V  R  O  A  A  E  L  V  T  Y  Y  C  V  E
O  P  A  N  N  X  H  I  U  U  S  R  F  I  D
O  X  M  I  Y  F  T  E  T  N  H  U  I  L  Y
D  V  T  R  O  D  D  E  N  M  A  N  R  A  U
B  A  E  E  Z  C  X  N  X  U  D  R  H  T  M
L  X  T  D  E  A  X  E  T  A  N  O  O  R  A
Y  J  I  I  S  A  I  C  I  L  E  F  Q  S  S
Y  C  B  R  O  D  I  D  L  O  G  L  L  A  A
H  T  E  B  A  Z  I  L  E  N  E  E  U  Q  B
O  Y  T  H  G  I  L  E  D  E  L  B  U  O  D
```

ALL GOLD	JACK WOOD	PRICELESS
ASHRAM	LATINA	QUEEN ELIZABETH
BRIDE	LEGEND	RIO SAMBA
DEAREST	LUNA ROSA	SEXY REXY
DENMAN	LUXOR	TABASCO
DOUBLE DELIGHT	MARY ROSE	TEXAS
FELICIA	MYRIAM	THE FAIRY
IDOLE	PEACE	TRUST

Discover a path to the image in the middle of this maze. Start at the entrance at the top.

 "The beginnings of all things are small."

Cicero

One of these barrels of apples is different from
the rest. Can you spot the odd one out?

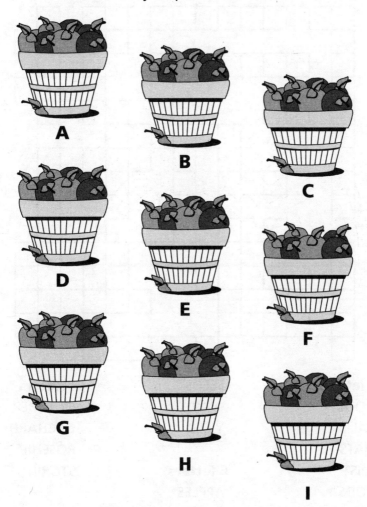

"Always I will take another step.
If that is of no avail I will take
another, and yet another. In truth, one
step at a time is not too difficult."

Og Mandino

The words are provided, but can you fit them all in the grid?

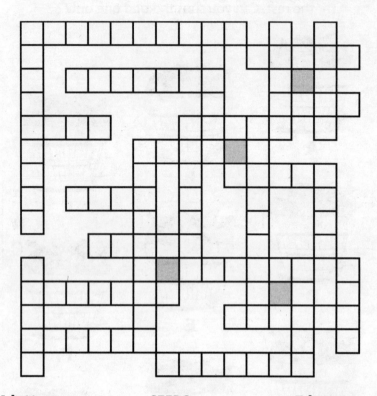

4 letters
COOL
FALL
HATS
MIST
PODS
RAIN

5 letters
ACORN
CROPS
FOGGY
FRUIT
SCARF

SEEDS
WINDY
YIELD

6 letters
APPLES
ASTERS
GLOOMY
GOLDEN

7 letters
OCTOBER
ORCHARD
ROSEHIP
STORING

9 letters
DECIDUOUS
HALLOWEEN
MUSHROOMS

10 letters
MICHAELMAS

Can you find all of the listed words hidden in the grid?
They may run forward or backward, in either a
horizontal, vertical or diagonal direction.

```
E C S C P S A P W C R H W T G
N E E B F G E B S Q P I H G N
W O R L A T U A S H B G Y A I
O A B P E S F R O L I C I R D
D A T F S B H N S N O Y R D D
E Y N S Y H R D G W Y B E E E
O E K R O C C A S I O N U N W
H F A C B E T N T P I C N I C
K V E Q I S M C C I N K I L M
E Y X S R G C E K T O R O I S
G H O O T E N A N N Y N N A O
A J E S H I N D I G W W Q S I
L J E L D Z V S O C I A L S R
A L L U A U B A N Q U E T A E
I G B I Y C E I L I D H R W E
```

BANQUET	FROLIC	REUNION
BARN DANCE	GALA	SHINDIG
BASH	GARDEN	SOCIAL
BIRTHDAY	HOEDOWN	SOIREE
CEILIDH	HOOTENANNY	SPREE
CELEBRATION	OCCASION	STAG NIGHT
FESTIVAL	PICNIC	WASSAIL
FETE	RAVE	WEDDING

109

Arroword

Enter the answer to each clue, one letter per square, in the direction indicated by the arrows. When completed, rearrange the letters in the shaded squares to spell out a word appropriate to the theme of this book.

Askew	▼	Red dye	▼	Chief magistrate of Venice or Genoa, historically	Moved rapidly	Old-fashioned affirmative answer	Female birds	▼
United Nations agency (inits) ▶		▼		Mound raised to prevent flooding	▼	▼		
Jamaican music style ▶							Mousse	
▶		(shaded)		Tatters ▶			▼	
"Old Lang ___", New Year's Eve song	Total distance covered by a motor vehicle		Victory	Foot lever		Fireside mat		Exclamation of pleasure in anticipation of food
Revealing supreme skill ▶	▼		▼	▼ (shaded)		▼		▼
Location, whereabouts		Official literary language of Pakistan ▶				(shaded)	Narrow backstreet	
▶					Collective noun for whales ▶		▼	(shaded)
Assigned to a station	Sealed metal storage container ▶					" ___ Maria", prayer to the Virgin Mary		Strong, angry emotion
▶	(shaded)				___ Baba ▶	▼		▼ (shaded)
Closely packed		Drool ▶						
▶					Organ of sight ▶			

Place one of the numbers from 1 to 9 into every empty cell so that each row, each column and each 3x3 block contains all the numbers from 1 to 9.

6		3		7			2	
8		1					5	4
	7	9	1	5				
		2			8			1
7	8		4		6		9	3
3			7			5		
				4	1	6	8	
5	4					9		2
	9			6		3		7

"Nor need we power or splendor, wide hall or lordly dome;

The good, the true, the tender – these form wealth of home."

Sarah J. Hale

Can you find all of the listed words hidden in the grid?
They may run forward or backward, in either a
horizontal, vertical or diagonal direction.

```
S M T X Q V S L I E V E H T Y
T U O R E S C A P E Y S P Y G
O X E R I G Y Y W A E P P D Y
P Z J D L F M H V A D V E N T
G R I Y A D L O S G O R F N N
I L I D H M H E N M H K Y U E
R S B V T S A Y S T S I N Z L
L Z A F A E M Y O Y T R H E P
S R W L X T L L A E T A C L X
L G L I O V E X P E L I N O D
R I L C I M T L O C D I O G U
Q E P A A K E L I B R E L Q O
D H A C L O U D S V B S M A N
F O O R P E P K I H E L E N G
N I Q O Q R P I K Z M S I M Q
```

ADVENT	FROGS	PRIVATE LIVES
AMADEUS	GALILEO	PROOF
ATHALIE	GYPSY	SALOME
CAMELOT	HAMLET	SYLVIA
CLOUDS	HELEN	TANGO
EGMONT	LE CID	THE VEIL
ESCAPE	MEDEA	TOP GIRLS
EXILED	PLENTY	TRIFLES

The words are provided, but can you fit them all in the grid?

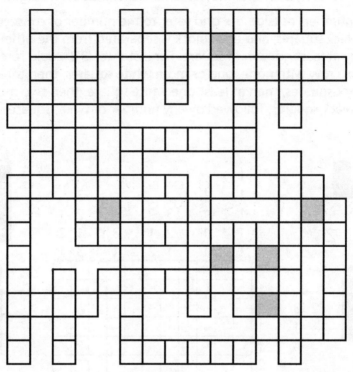

3 letters
HOP

4 letters
ARUM
HEMP
IRIS
LILY
ROSE
RUSH

5 letters
ASTER
OXLIP
POPPY
STOCK

6 letters
BRYONY
FAT HEN
NETTLE
SORREL

8 letters
ASPHODEL
DAFFODIL
PLANTAIN
PURSLANE
TOADFLAX

9 letters
DANDELION
DIAPENSIA
PIMPERNEL

10 letters
SNAPDRAGON

12 letters
LADY'S SLIPPER

Place all twelve of the pieces into the grid. Any may be rotated or flipped over, but none may touch another, not even diagonally.

The numbers outside the grid refer to the number of consecutive black squares; and each block is separated from the others by at least one white square. For instance, '3 2' could refer to a row with none, one or more white squares, then three black squares, then at least one white square, then two more black squares, followed by any number of white squares.

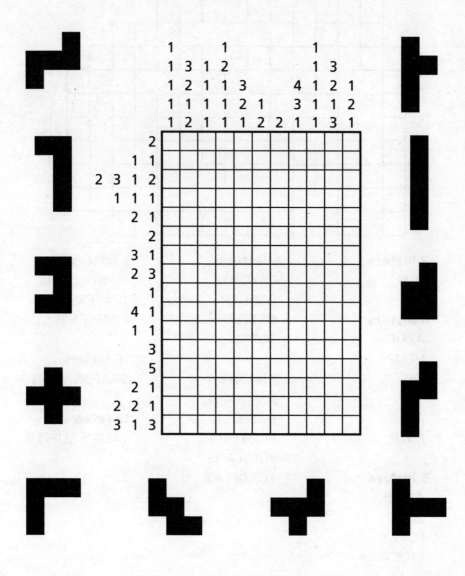

First solve the clues. All of the solutions end with the letter in the middle of the circle, and in every word an additional letter is in place. When the puzzle is complete, reading clockwise around the shaded ring of letters will reveal the names of two birds.

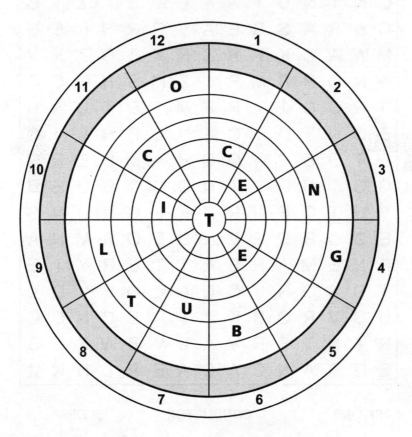

1 Waterproof garment
2 Responsive to orders
3 Financially ruined
4 Lacking general education or knowledge
5 Substance that can provide energy
6 Triumphant

7 Heated debate
8 Slingshot
9 Unit of electrical power
10 Abandoned, falling in ruins
11 Form of transport, plane
12 Cylindrical mass of earth voided by a burrowing creature

Answer: _____ **and** _____

Can you find all of the listed words hidden in the grid?
They may run forward or backward, in either a
horizontal, vertical or diagonal direction.

```
G N I N U T O K L Y S F Z T C
C B R A S S E A V G R H R E G
M W A C K F B S N X E O Z K V
A N O R P M R I Z M S H O C C
J R S O I I R F M I O T U A H
E O N T D T C S N E P H L J O
L T O E S W O C H A M B E R R
O C I N O Y I N O O O B O E U
V U T O P N R N E L C D D N S
E D C B R S V N D S O A M N A
R N E M A H B A T T E R Y I E
T O S O N J C E L L O F Y D L
U C V R O B K Z T R E C N O C
R I N T E R V A L V B W Z P B
E G R A N C A S A E P L N N J
```

BARITONE	CONDUCTOR	SCORE
BATTERY	DINNER JACKET	SECTIONS
BRASS	GRAN CASA	SOPRANO
CELLO	INTERVAL	STRINGS
CHAMBER	LEADER	TIMBAL
CHORUS	OVERTURE	TROMBONE
COMPOSER	PICCOLO	TUNING
CONCERT	ROSIN	WOODWIND

The words are provided, but can you fit them all in the grid?

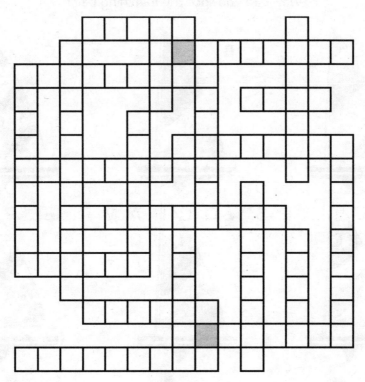

4 letters
CATS
DOGS

5 letters
CAKES
CANDY

6 letters
GRANNY
HORSES
SWEETS

7 letters
FLOWERS
INCENSE
KITTENS
SEAFOOD
WALKING

8 letters
DIAMONDS
GOOD FOOD
WEDDINGS

9 letters
CHAMPAGNE
CHRISTMAS
OPEN FIRES
SURPRISES

10 letters
TELEVISION

11 letters
SANDCASTLES

A Matching Pair

Only two of these boats are identical in every way. Can you spot the matching pair?

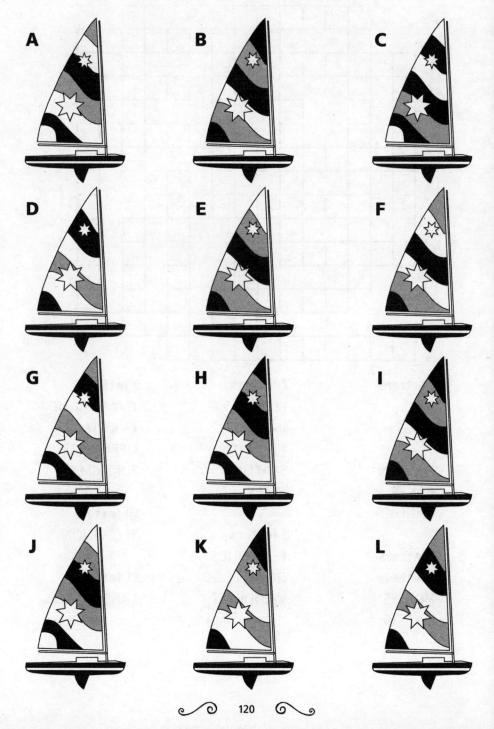

Can you find all of the listed words hidden in the grid?
They may run forward or backward, in either a
horizontal, vertical or diagonal direction.

```
W V I W E B E Q H S E M Y H T
N R Y H C D S A E P T I L P S
O U S I A D R S F P T S F L E
R E Z E M P L A O O R C E P V
F A S R B U E Y G Q G U N S O
F J G U P U H P S U R G N A L
A F S E L K C I P Z S Y E E C
S H Y P N T B K U E E Q L Z S
G Q O Y Z I A M C A R H V A Z
I A A N W M V N S O C U M I N
N C C E E T L T A L T S A L T
G R L A D Y P U O S E S W M X
E C Z S B R E H C H U T N E Y
R I T B E C U A S O T A M O T
P U S D N O M L A N C X K T F
```

ALMONDS	MACE	SPLIT PEAS
CHUTNEY	PEPPER	STOCK CUBES
CLOVES	PICKLES	SUGAR
CUMIN	PRUNES	SULTANAS
FENNEL	PULSES	THYME
GINGER	SAFFRON	TOMATO SAUCE
HERBS	SALT	VINEGAR
HONEY	SOUP	YEAST

Discover a path to the image in the middle of this maze. Start at the entrance at the top.

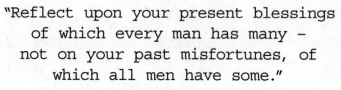

"Reflect upon your present blessings of which every man has many – not on your past misfortunes, of which all men have some."

Charles Dickens

The words are provided, but can you fit them all in the grid?

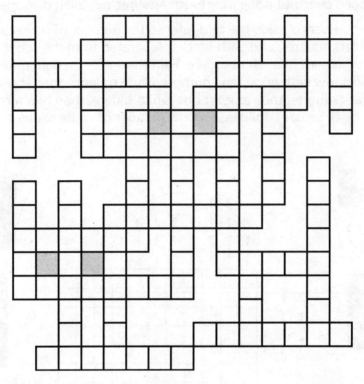

4 letters
PURL
ROWS
WOOL

5 letters
HANKS
NYLON
PLAIN
SOCKS
SPOOL
TWIST
YARNS

6 letters
CAST ON
COLLAR
JUMPER
REPEAT

7 letters
DROPPED
SELVAGE
SQUARES
SWEATER
TANK TOP
TENSION

8 letters
KNITTING
PRESSING
PULLOVER
STOCKING

9 letters
WAISTCOAT

Place all twelve of the pieces into the grid. Any may be rotated or flipped over, but none may touch another, not even diagonally.

The numbers outside the grid refer to the number of consecutive black squares; and each block is separated from the others by at least one white square. For instance, '3 2' could refer to a row with none, one or more white squares, then three black squares, then at least one white square, then two more black squares, followed by any number of white squares.

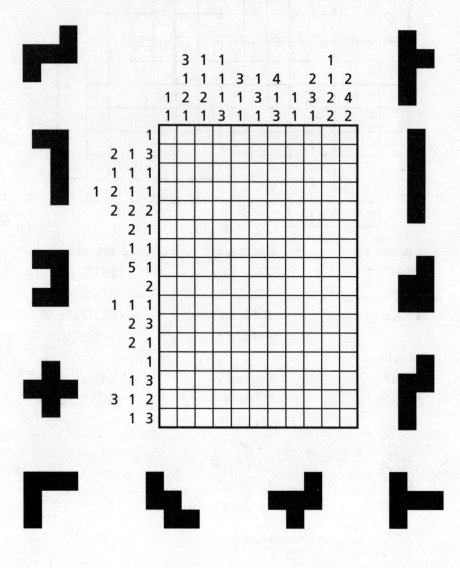

Place one of the numbers from 1 to 9 into every
empty cell so that each row, each column and each
3x3 block contains all the numbers from 1 to 9.

	1			4	2			6
9	6	2	5					
		3			6	8	7	
		6		5			2	7
		9	4		3	1		
4	5			6		9		
	8	5	7			2		
					8	7	5	1
2			9	3			4	

"The person who is developing freely
and naturally arrives at a spiritual
equilibrium in which he is master of his
actions, just as one who has acquired
physical poise can move freely."

Maria Montessori

Can you find all of the listed words hidden in the grid?
They may run forward or backward, in either a
horizontal, vertical or diagonal direction.

```
S O S E T O N E R U T C E L H
R D G T E V E P I C E R G D C
J J R I V R N D O W A S A W B
T O Z A F E U V B I J I S C N
E O U W C T N T X L L R S A O
R R D R U Y T V A L D E E L Y
O E H O N G A A E N K C M V U
C P D P L A R D G L G E T P B
S A R N A I L E H E O I O O Q
C P E J I R S A E T M P S S R
I M P D A M G T B T R T E T E
S A O O I O E O T E I I O C N
U X R N I A J R T R L N B A N
M E T D Y L R N M U J S G R A
D D R A C U O Y K N A H T D B
```

AUTOGRAPH	GREETING	RECEIPT
BANNER	JOURNAL	RECIPE
BIRTHDAY CARD	LABELS	REMINDER
DIARY	LECTURE NOTES	REPORT
ENVELOPE	LETTER	SIGNATURE
ESSAY	MESSAGE	THANK-YOU CARD
EXAM PAPER	MUSIC SCORE	TO-DO LIST
GIFT TAG	POSTCARD	WILL

The words are provided, but can you fit them all in the grid?

4 letters
BILL
FISH
MEAL
MEAT
MENU

5 letters
GLASS
GRILL
PARTY
SEATS
SWEET

6 letters
DINERS
DINNER
DRINKS
EATERY
NAPKIN
WAITER

7 letters
CUTLERY
STARTER

8 letters
LUNCHEON
WAITRESS

9 letters
BRASSERIE

10 letters
MAIN COURSE
VEGETARIAN

Which four shapes (two black and two white) can be fitted together to form the leaf shown here? The pieces may be rotated, but not flipped over.

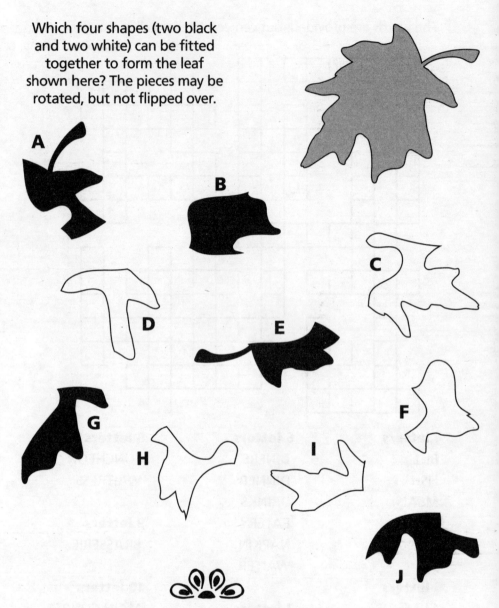

"Walk away quietly in any direction and taste the freedom of the mountaineer... Climb the mountains and get their good tidings. Nature's peace will flow into you as sunshine flows into trees."

John Muir

Place the listed words horizontally into the grid, so that when read from top left to bottom right, the letters in the shaded squares spell out the name of a vegetable. Some letters are already in place.

BRINJAL

HENBANE

LACTUCA

PRIMULA

SOURSOP

SPURREY

TURPETH

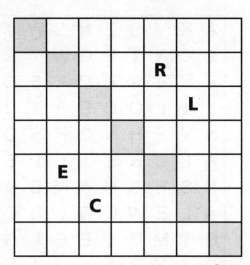

"The key is to keep company only with people who uplift you, whose presence calls forth your best."

Epictetus

Can you find all of the listed words hidden in the grid?
They may run forward or backward, in either a
horizontal, vertical or diagonal direction.

```
A  K  Y  S  Z  N  O  W  Y  L  L  I  D  G  B
L  C  R  T  E  Q  W  Y  R  B  O  R  A  G  E
L  H  E  J  K  M  F  S  R  A  L  T  B  E  G
I  I  L  O  C  E  A  I  U  N  O  C  T  M  D
N  V  E  H  N  G  R  S  C  N  B  I  G  T  N
A  L  C  N  E  I  L  L  E  E  E  N  A  U  C
V  S  E  S  H  A  M  B  Q  S  R  N  A  N  I
A  L  E  W  Q  Q  L  U  C  C  G  A  L  C  N
Q  T  M  O  S  E  C  L  C  E  A  M  L  A  C
D  X  Y  R  X  A  O  A  L  Q  M  O  S  S  D
A  Z  H  T  C  V  F  I  P  D  O  N  P  S  E
N  J  T  Y  E  A  C  F  G  E  T  H  I  I  R
I  M  U  S  T  A  R  D  R  H  R  T  C  A  F
S  F  M  V  J  Z  X  O  I  O  L  A  E  Y  O
E  S  E  V  I  H  C  V  L  J  N  G  H  R  V
```

ALLSPICE	CHIVES	NUTMEG
ANGELICA	CINNAMON	SAFFRON
ANISE	CLOVES	SAGE
BERGAMOT	CUMIN	SENNA
BORAGE	CURRY	SESAME
CAPER	DILL	ST JOHN'S WORT
CASSIA	FENNEL	THYME
CELERY	MUSTARD	VANILLA

The words are provided, but can you fit them all in the grid?

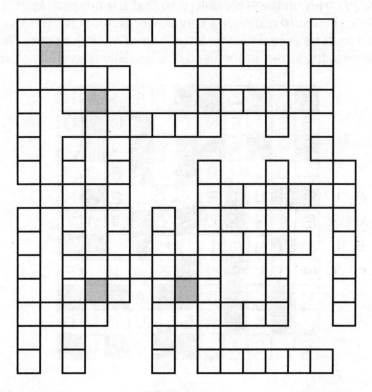

4 letters
PLUG
SINK
SOAP
SUDS

5 letters
BIDET
FLOSS
FLUSH
RAZOR

6 letters
HOT TAP
LOOFAH
MAKE-UP
MOUSSE
SPONGE

7 letters
AEROSOL
BATH MAT
BATHTUB
CABINET
CISTERN
COLOGNE

FLANNEL
SHAMPOO

9 letters
HAIRBRUSH

10 letters
TOOTHBRUSH
TOOTHPASTE

Ladle the letters from the soup tureen and fit one into each of the 26 bowls on the table below, so that the finished result is a complete crossword containing English words. All of the letters in the tureen must be used – thus no letter is used more than once. When rearranged, the letters in the filled bowls spell out a variety of apple.

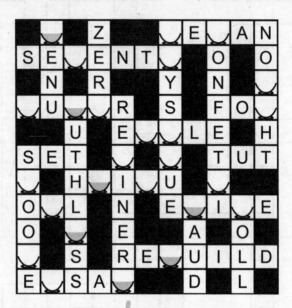

A B C D E F G H I J K
L M N O P Q R S
T U V W X Y Z

"Knowing others is intelligence;
knowing yourself is true wisdom.
Mastering others is strength;
mastering yourself is true power."

Lao Tzu

First solve the clues. All of the solutions end with the letter in the middle of the circle, and in every word an additional letter is in place. When the puzzle is complete, reading clockwise around the shaded ring of letters will reveal the names of two birds.

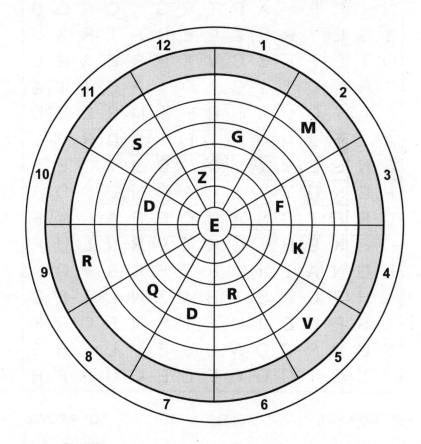

1 Means of verbal communication

2 Inoculate against disease

3 Implement for shaping, used in manicure (4,4)

4 Chain worn as an ornament

5 All people

6 Largest of the Canary Islands

7 Lower jawbone

8 Enough

9 Receive an academic degree

10 Heaven

11 Protect from heat, cold, noise, etc

12 Appropriate (especially money) fraudulently for one's own use

Answer: _____ **and** _____

Can you find all of the listed words hidden in the grid?
They may run forward or backward, in either a
horizontal, vertical or diagonal direction.

```
N I K E M A R T R G K Q G Q B
Y S E Y R E Z E E R F T R X G
Q T E F K Z C V X P R E A S L
T R L Q I I C I Q I P C T I A
E A T C U N L R H I M E E E D
A I T J N A K T E T S D R V L
S N E D R Y V D O D Q T O E E
P E K D Y Y I P A P N E O O A
O R E T G S A U C E P A N V F
O R K E H E G K T P R N L H E
N G N A T J I R T F K B P O N
N H S C K S I H W Z N L I B C
L S P U O J U F I S H F O R K
S O U P B O W L S E V L E H S
Y X C I C O F F E E C U P B H
```

BREAD KNIFE	KETTLE	SOUP BOWL
COFFEE CUP	LADLE	STOVE
COLANDER	LARDER	STRAINER
FISH FORK	PIE DISH	TEACUP
FOOD MIXER	RAMEKIN	TEAPOT
FREEZER	SAUCEPAN	TEASPOON
GRATER	SHELVES	TRIVET
JUICER	SIEVE	WHISK

Every clue in this puzzle is an anagram leading to a single-word solution. Correctly solve the anagram on each level of the pyramid and another word will appear, reading down the central column of bricks.

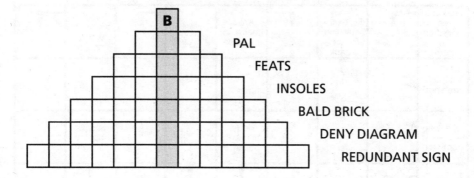

PAL
FEATS
INSOLES
BALD BRICK
DENY DIAGRAM
REDUNDANT SIGN

Using the letters in the Wordwheel, you have ten minutes to find as many words as possible of three letters or more, none of which may be plurals, foreign words or proper nouns. Each word must contain the central letter and no letters can be used more than once per word unless they appear in different spokes of the wheel. There is at least one nine-letter word to be found.

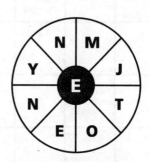

Nine-letter word(s):

_____

"Let no one be slow to seek wisdom when he is young nor weary in the search of it when he has grown old. For no age is too early or too late for the health of the soul."

Epicurus

Arroword

Enter the answer to each clue, one letter per square, in the direction indicated by the arrows. When completed, rearrange the letters in the shaded squares to spell out a word appropriate to the theme of this book.

Bee-house or collection of beehives ▼	Money-dispensing machine (outside a bank) ▼		▼	Ant or beetle, for example	Collection of maps ▼		Bundles bound for storage or transport ▼	
Italian cured pork ►	▼							
Of a thing / Door sign ►				Deter-mined in advance	Capital of Peru		Metallic tapping sound	
►				▼	▼		▼	
Process for obtaining an objective	Emer-gency / Banded ►							
►	▼					Doglike		Distance covered by a step
Concur	Secreting structure in animals	Fires / Literary com-position ►				▼		▼
►	▼	▼			Stretches (out)		Large container for liquids	
Hearer ► / Tight-fitting hats					▼		▼	
►				Bird of New Zealand ►				
Straigh-tened out ► / Small whirlpool								
►				Withered ►				

Place one of the numbers from 1 to 9 into every
empty cell so that each row, each column and each
3x3 block contains all the numbers from 1 to 9.

9			7	1	8			
1				5		7	6	9
4			6		9			
	9		4		5	8		
6		4				3		2
		8	2		3		5	
			1		2			5
8	2	7		4				1
			9	3	7			8

"Remember that man lives only in the
present, in this fleeting instant; all
the rest of his life is either past
and gone, or not yet revealed."

Marcus Aurelius

Can you find all of the listed words hidden in the grid?
They may run forward or backward, in either a
horizontal, vertical or diagonal direction.

O	N	I	K	G	N	Y	V	G	N	B	D	A	H	M
W	E	H	W	P	T	O	F	O	G	N	A	M	A	Q
O	D	C	M	I	B	F	M	O	N	G	B	T	Z	F
X	R	R	O	X	K	E	L	M	H	O	A	F	E	B
N	Z	A	B	C	L	D	E	R	I	U	Q	I	L	E
A	G	E	N	H	O	A	Q	J	Q	S	Z	L	N	N
C	S	P	O	G	T	N	Y	M	Y	M	R	B	U	I
E	N	I	G	R	E	B	U	A	A	Z	W	E	T	T
P	O	L	I	V	E	K	Q	T	P	F	A	R	P	N
I	L	G	X	D	J	W	J	U	R	A	Y	T	Z	E
E	E	Q	V	I	C	T	O	R	I	A	P	L	U	M
N	M	U	G	O	U	Q	A	N	C	N	D	A	T	E
U	H	I	A	U	H	U	I	Y	O	J	C	X	D	L
R	F	L	L	U	S	D	I	F	T	L	S	E	P	C
P	L	G	R	A	P	E	F	R	U	I	T	U	Z	T

APRICOT	HAZELNUT	ORANGE
AUBERGINE	KIWI	PAPAYA
CLEMENTINE	KUMQUAT	PEAR
COCONUT	LEMON	PECAN
DATE	LIME	PERSIMMON
FIG	MANGO	PRUNE
FILBERT	MELON	QUINCE
GRAPEFRUIT	OLIVE	VICTORIA PLUM

The words are provided, but can you fit them all in the grid?

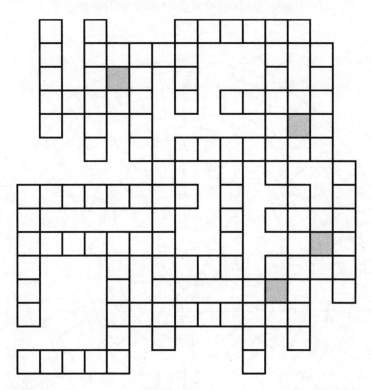

4 letters
BARS
CAKE
DARK
MILK
RICH

5 letters
CANDY
CHIPS
COCOA
FUDGE
PLAIN
SAUCE
SWEET

6 letters
BITTER
DOUBLE
ECLAIR
FONDUE
KISSES
SMOOTH

7 letters
BISCUIT
CARAMEL
LIQUEUR
TRUFFLE

8 letters
BEVERAGE
BROWNIES

9 letters
DIGESTIVE

Discover a path to the image in the middle of this maze. Start at the entrance at the top.

"Only by listening inwardly in a fresh and open way will you discern at any given time what most serves your healing and freedom."

Tara Brach

Place all twelve of the pieces into the grid. Any may be rotated or flipped over, but none may touch another, not even diagonally.

The numbers outside the grid refer to the number of consecutive black squares; and each block is separated from the others by at least one white square. For instance, '3 2' could refer to a row with none, one or more white squares, then three black squares, then at least one white square, then two more black squares, followed by any number of white squares.

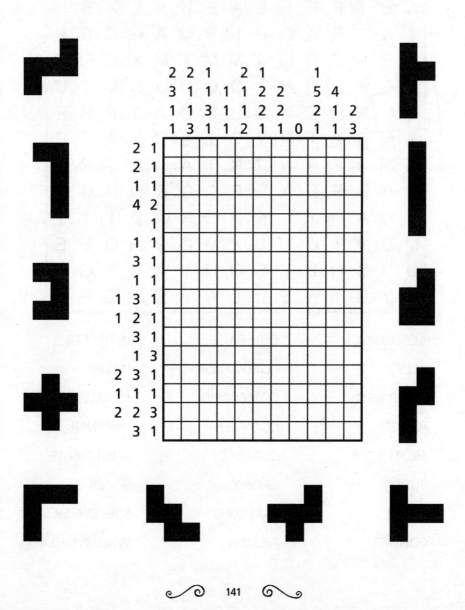

Can you find all of the listed words hidden in the grid?
They may run forward or backward, in either a
horizontal, vertical or diagonal direction.

```
V P E G E U G A E L L O C V T
I R N C B X L I R E A O E S E
E T A M I T N I E H E T I D S
A E T F E L E A E U A L A B H
I N J R A O P L P M A R C R P
D P E B O M J M M Y M X O O S
N G A D F H I O O O U S M T U
O F N R E V O L C C I J P H P
I M B Z T R Y C I S C X A E P
N M D F R N R N T A A A T R O
A B U F E A E E O O R D R G R
P U A H Y L R R S R W Z I I T
M D V I C L L K U O C M O E E
O D S Q L Y S O H Y A V T G R
C Y B T W E L L W I S H E R L
```

ACCOMPLICE	COLLEAGUE	INTIMATE
ALLY	COMPANION	LOVER
ALTER EGO	COMPATRIOT	LOYALIST
AMIGO	COMPEER	PARTNER
BROTHER	COMRADE	ROOMMATE
BUDDY	CRONY	SISTER
CHUM	FAMILIAR	SUPPORTER
COHORT	FELLOW	WELL-WISHER

The words are provided, but can you fit them all in the grid?

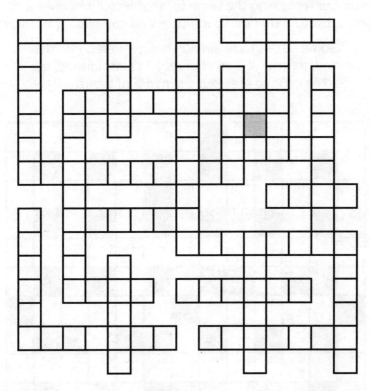

4 letters
MACE
SAGE
SALT
SOUP

5 letters
CUMIN
HONEY
SUGAR
YEAST

6 letters
FENNEL
GINGER
NUTMEG
PEPPER
PICKLE
PRUNES

7 letters
MUSTARD
RAISINS
TREACLE

8 letters
STUFFING
TARRAGON

9 letters
SPLIT PEAS

10 letters
DRIED FRUIT
SALAD CREAM
STOCK CUBES

Codeword

Every letter in this crossword has been replaced by a number, the number remaining the same for that letter wherever it occurs. Can you substitute numbers for letters and complete the crossword?

Some letters have already been entered into the grid, to help you on your way. When finished, use the code to spell out the name of a butterfly.

14	9	25	13	20	■	5	20	21	11	22	9	6
16	■	2	■	13	■	13	■	15	■	20	■	20
11	1	10	13	17	25	26	■	2	2	13	12	13
20	■	3	■	21	■	26	■	3	■	1	■	11
19	25	1	6	20	3	2	21	24	11	3	14	12
18	■	■	13	■	■	25	■	11	■	6	■	13
■	8	3	23	25	2	■	4	25	5	25	2	■
12	■	12	■	16	■	10	■	■	25	■	■	7
13	8	8	20	21	8	20	3	13	6	3	21	1
20	■	25	■	1	■	3	■	16	■	22	■	3
6	21	20	14	21	■	25	13	20	8	2	11	22
18	■	3	■	12	■	1	■	25	■	21	■	9
20	25	2	13	18	25	26	■	14	9	21 O	20 R	6 T

Row labels (left): A B C D E F G H I J K L M
Right labels: N O P Q R S T U V W X Y Z

1	2	3	4	5	6 T	7	8	9	10	11	12	13
14	15	16	17	18	19	20 R	21 O	22	23	24	25	26

Answer

8	25	13	16	21	16	7

One of these candles is different from the rest. Can you spot the odd one out?

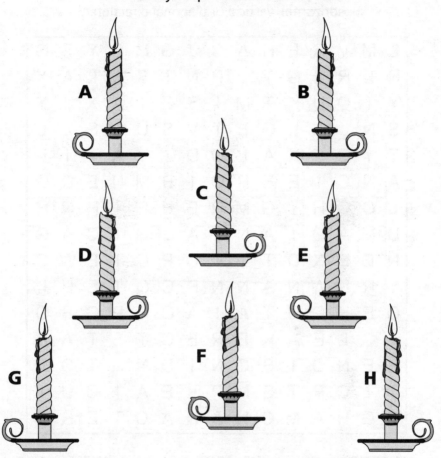

"We may wish to set aside some time for a retreat, a day of mindfulness, when we can walk slowly, smile, drink tea with a friend, enjoy being together as if we are the happiest people on Earth."

Thich Nhat Hanh

Wordsearch: DRUIDS

Can you find all of the listed words hidden in the grid?
They may run forward or backward, in either a
horizontal, vertical or diagonal direction.

```
C M V R F H A C J G M S Y S G
R L R L G T I P N I S W L A X
Y I O U K T M I S E I A X J Y
S N L A L G L T V S U L S Z L
T Y O E K A L O D T Y A T I L
A N C I E E R O I B M N E D O
L O O H T G M R E H E I R N H
D M A O I A N L A I G T C A G
N E E X D T T I C P C I E W C
Y R R W N A N N R C Q I S H L
O E K C N T A I A O I P G S O
I C L E A K E R E C T S T A B
S E N O T S G N I D N A T S M
T I C R T E M P L E A I C U I
O G H A M C H A R A C T E R S
```

ANCIENT	HEALING	PRIEST
ASH WAND	HOLLY	RITUALS
BELTANE	IMBOLC	SACRED
CELTIC	INCANTATION	SAMHAIN
CEREMONY	LUGH	SECRETS
CLOAK	MAGIC	STANDING STONES
CRYSTAL	MISTLETOE	TEMPLE
GROVES	OGHAM CHARACTERS	WISDOM

The words are provided, but can you fit them all in the grid?

4 letters	**6 letters**	**8 letters**
CAFE	AVIARY	FOUNTAIN
LAKE	BUSHES	PAVILION
	PEOPLE	
5 letters	SEESAW	**9 letters**
FENCE	STATUE	BANDSTAND
GRASS	TENNIS	
LAWNS		**10 letters**
PATHS	**7 letters**	PLAYGROUND
PONDS	BENCHES	
ROSES	FLOWERS	
SEATS		
SWANS		
TREES		

Place the answers in order across the horizontal rows.
When completed correctly, reading down each of the
shaded columns will reveal the name of a plant.

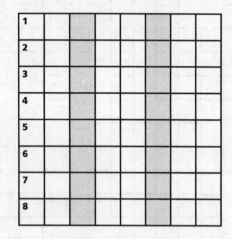

1 Blossomed
2 Sugar found in fruit and honey
3 Throw overboard
4 Advancement
5 Aromatic bark of a tree
 used as a spice
6 Alert, watchful
7 Bushy-tailed arboreal rodent
8 Purple gemstone

"We must let go of the
life we have planned,
so as to accept the one
that is waiting for us."

Joseph Campbell

Fit the listed words into the grid below (one letter is already in place), then rearrange the letters in the shaded squares to form the name of a flower.

3 letters	4 letters		5 letters	
APE	BARB	OOZE	BANJO	ROWED
DID	BEAN	PITY	BEIGE	SALTY
DOT	BRAE	SOYA	CLAMP	TWIST
NOT	DOSE	TERM	DOGMA	VALET
PEN	EVER	USED	ERECT	VOICE
POP	MENU	YARD	PANIC	WHEAT
SAG				
SHE				

"This is a moment of suffering. Suffering is part of life. May I be kind to myself in this moment. May I give myself the compassion I need."

Kristin Neff

Can you find all of the listed words hidden in the grid?
They may run forward or backward, in either a
horizontal, vertical or diagonal direction.

E	R	S	S	E	N	S	S	E	L	E	M	I	T	E
Z	E	E	E	V	I	T	C	E	P	S	R	E	P	S
S	V	I	G	I	L	A	N	C	E	S	E	M	F	C
A	H	T	I	A	C	W	V	H	K	E	R	F	O	T
N	L	F	H	T	R	Q	I	I	K	N	A	N	N	H
C	P	U	U	G	L	D	S	S	F	C	C	E	D	O
T	U	F	F	Y	I	W	I	Z	D	E	M	M	R	U
U	G	O	U	D	T	L	O	X	N	O	Q	O	S	G
A	N	C	F	R	E	I	N	T	M	S	M	G	B	H
R	I	U	R	B	W	E	R	E	F	N	N	G	S	T
Y	N	S	E	Y	X	A	H	A	R	I	M	P	L	F
O	E	O	E	F	T	T	Y	M	L	H	A	Q	P	U
Z	P	U	D	I	N	D	L	E	F	C	A	Q	O	L
T	O	L	O	I	H	A	E	P	E	A	C	E	M	G
H	K	N	M	V	C	F	Y	T	I	N	E	R	E	S

CALM	HEEDFUL	SERENITY
CARE	IN THE MOMENT	SOUL
CLARITY	LIGHT	SPACE
CONCENTRATION	OPENING UP	THOUGHTFUL
ESSENCE	PEACE	TIMELESSNESS
FEELINGS	PERSPECTIVE	VIGILANCE
FOCUS	REGARD	VISION
FREEDOM	SANCTUARY	WISDOM

Straightforward clues are presented with the crossword grid but the clues are in alphabetical order and the grid is minus its black squares. You need to black out some of the squares, resulting in a filled symmetrical crossword, as well as fill in the missing letters. When finished, rearrange the letters in the shaded squares (which must not be blacked out) to spell out the name of a wild flower.

I	C	E	B	E	R		E	M	O	T	T	O
C	H	E	E	R	E	D	C	O	V	E	R	S
D	I	E	T	A	M	U	R	D	E	R		R
S	N	O	W	Y	A	M	U	E	R	A	M	P
C	A	R	E		R	E	E	R	T	U	B	E
O	B	R	E	A	K	I	L	N	O	S	L	Y
A	G		N	Y	I	N	K	W	A		E	R
T	R	A	I	N	T	Y	P	I	C	A	L	O
S	A	G	A	O	E		E	R	C	I	S	E
S	N	O	R	T	N	A	S	O	O	T	H	S
T	I	R	E	S	O	M	E	N	U	P		N
S	T	U	N	A	N	I	T	A	N	G	V	E
P	E	D	A		I	P	A	N	T	H	E	R

Clues:

Acute pain

Amid

Coarse-grained rock, often pink

Criminal who commits homicide

Saying or slogan of a sect or political group

Former Spanish monetary unit

High-quality porcelain

Hollow cylinder

Lacking mercy

Large feline of tropical America

Large mass of frozen water

Lever operated with the foot

Long detailed story

Keep fit, work out

Make mention of

Open and observable

Prescribed selection of foods

Projection shaped to fit into a mortise

Push roughly

Shake with fear

Situated at the top of

Statement

Structure for open-air sports

Tedious

Unworried

Vacillate

"Happiness is very simple and minimal."

Tablo

First solve the clues. All of the solutions end with the letter in the middle of the circle, and in every word an additional letter is in place. When the puzzle is complete, reading clockwise around the shaded ring of letters will reveal a word appropriate to the theme of this book.

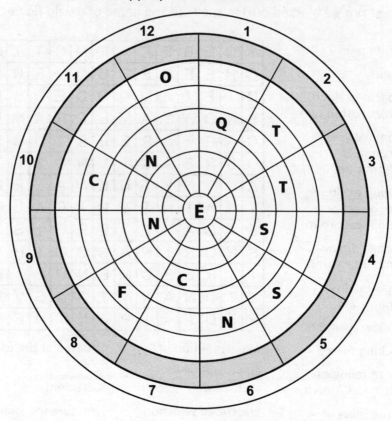

1 Sufficient

2 Free from a twisted state

3 Slow-moving reptile

4 Good-looking

5 Rough guess

6 Having no intelligible meaning

7 Be prudent or watchful (4,4)

8 Having no limits in time, space or magnitude

9 Start

10 Addition

11 Three-sided figure

12 National Park in California, famed for its waterfalls

Answer: _____

Place one of the numbers from 1 to 9 into every empty cell so that each row, each column and each 3x3 block contains all the numbers from 1 to 9.

8			6			9	3	
6				5	3		1	2
		1	4				5	
	8			2		1		3
		2	3		6	4		
7		5		4			6	
	9				7	3		
1	7		5	9				8
	6	4			1			7

"The most difficult times for many of us are the ones we give ourselves."

Pema Chödrön

Can you find all of the listed words hidden in the grid?
They may run forward or backward, in either a
horizontal, vertical or diagonal direction.

```
T Y T E T A G I T S E V N I S
U B L T H E C I T O N E Y F T
O C O C E W E C F G H I G D A
E M O L E Y E H B Q O C Q R R
K E G C U P E G T T T H F A E
A O Y P S E U U A U Z V I G A
M Y G N N G D R P K U U X E Q
E V I T F Y E Z A G G L A R E
S X B U F E K G M E L C T L M
S I A E P C T A K E A P E E K
H Z G M E S J P H O W E I V Y
N S Z H I Z U E C R Q G U J D
A Z C O T N F S M O Z Y Z S U
X U V A P K E M D O R S P O T
C O A S N E S U R E P E E P S
```

CHECK	INSPECT	REGARD
ESPY	INVESTIGATE	SCAN
EXAMINE	MAKE OUT	SIGHT
EYE UP	NOTICE	SPOT
FIXATE	OGLE	STARE
GAPE	PEEP	STUDY
GAZE	PEER AT	TAKE A PEEK
GLARE	PERUSE	VIEW

Which four shapes (two black and two white) can be fitted together to form the swan shown here? The pieces may be rotated, but not flipped over.

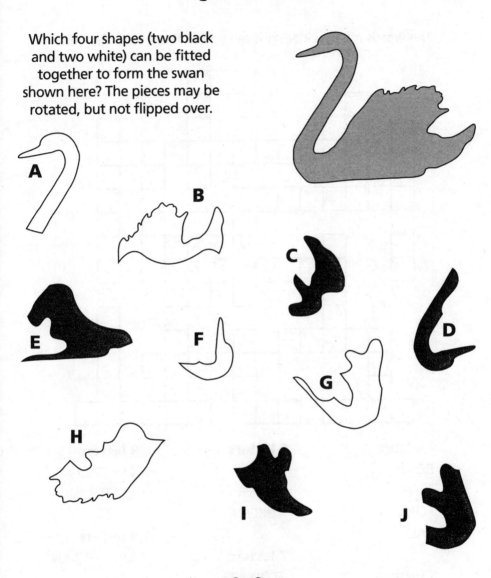

"No thing great is created suddenly, any more than a bunch of grapes or a fig. If you tell me that you desire a fig, I answer you that there must be time. Let it first blossom, then bear fruit, then ripen."

Epictetus

The words are provided, but can you fit them all in the grid?

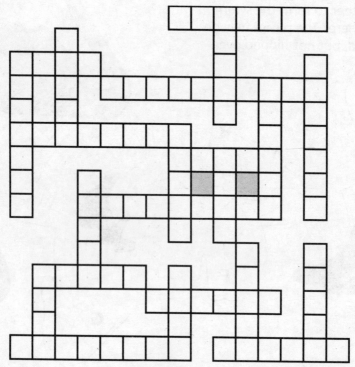

4 letters
BOWL
DISH
FORK
SALT

5 letters
BREAD
FRUIT
GLASS
KNIFE
LADLE
PLATE
SAUCE
SPOON

6 letters
NAPKIN
PEPPER
TUREEN

7 letters
FLOWERS
KETCHUP
MUSTARD

8 letters
PLACE MAT
WATER JUG

9 letters
LAZY SUSAN

10 letters
WINE BOTTLE

Discover a path to the image in the middle of this
maze. Start at the entrance at the top.

"If you only have one smile in you,
give it to the people you love.
Don't be surly at home, then go out
in the street and start grinning
'Good morning' at total strangers."

Maya Angelou

Can you find all of the listed words hidden in the grid?
They may run forward or backward, in either a
horizontal, vertical or diagonal direction.

```
N M B S A S E M A C A G O N E
J S U I T T C D B O L E R O T
X U E J U Z O P A R X C Y N O
D E N A Y A G Y R C D K U A X
F H L G N M P V B H A T P N I
I P R E A B A O D O C F O A U
R R O B C N U T L R X N E T Q
E O D T U O H C A L A E L N N
B K E A N R R C Y M O N L E O
I O O K K R K S W X F I E V D
R Z J B G E P M A L W D S A P
D N E M R A C F W I R N I L W
Z A I V L Y S E Y Y R O G O C
P T D S E C O N S E L E H S L
P E T R O U C H K A V V Q D O
```

AGON	FIREBIRD	MANON
ANYUTA	GAYANE	NUTCRACKER
APOLLO	GISELLE	ONDINE
BOLERO	JEUX	ORPHEUS
CARMEN	JOB	PETROUCHKA
CHOUT	LA VENTANA	RODEO
DON QUIXOTE	LE CORSAIRE	SYLVIA
FACADE	LES NOCES	TOY BOX

Place all twelve of the pieces into the grid. Any may be rotated or flipped over, but none may touch another, not even diagonally.

The numbers outside the grid refer to the number of consecutive black squares; and each block is separated from the others by at least one white square. For instance, '3 2' could refer to a row with none, one or more white squares, then three black squares, then at least one white square, then two more black squares, followed by any number of white squares.

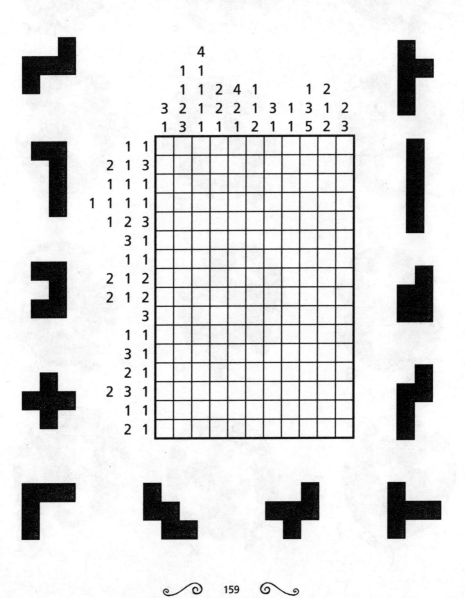

A Matching Pair

Only two of these swirling balloons are identical in every way. Can you spot the matching pair?

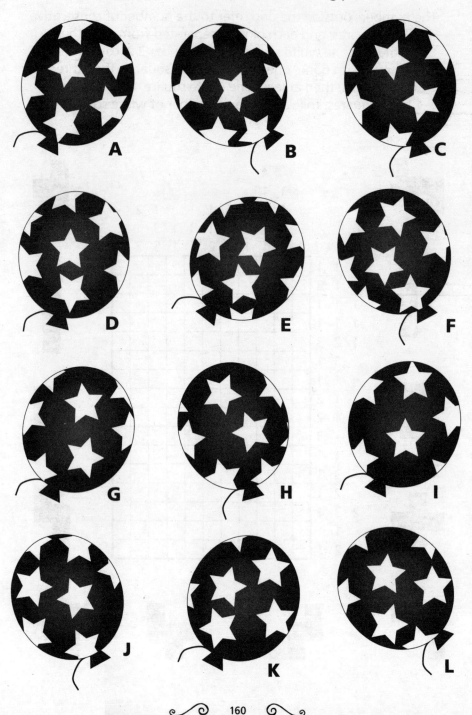

Ladle the letters from the soup tureen and fit one into each of the 26 bowls on the table below, so that the finished result is a complete crossword containing English words. All of the letters in the tureen must be used – thus no letter is used more than once. When rearranged, the letters in the filled bowls spell out a variety of tomato.

"The key in letting go is practice.
Each time we let go, we disentangle
ourselves from our expectations and begin
to experience things as they are."

Sharon Salzberg

160   Pyragram

Every clue in this puzzle is an anagram leading to a single-word solution. Correctly solve the anagram on each level of the pyramid and another word will appear, reading down the central column of bricks.

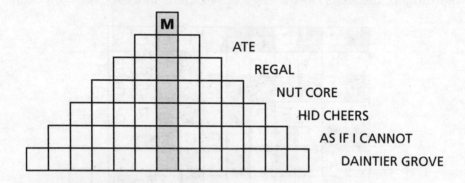

ATE

REGAL

NUT CORE

HID CHEERS

AS IF I CANNOT

DAINTIER GROVE

161   Word Wheel

Using the letters in the Wordwheel, you have ten minutes to find as many words as possible of three letters or more, none of which may be plurals, foreign words or proper nouns. Each word must contain the central letter and no letters can be used more than once per word unless they appear in different spokes of the wheel. There is at least one nine-letter word to be found.

Nine-letter word(s):

_____

"The whole world is a series of miracles, but we're so used to them we call them ordinary things."

Hans Christian Andersen

The words are provided, but can you fit them all in the grid?

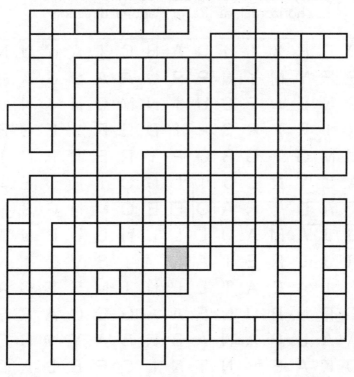

5 letters
BASIL
ORRIS
SENNA

6 letters
BALSAM
GARLIC
GINGER
LOVAGE
SORREL
SUNDEW

7 letters
COMFREY
GINSENG
SAFFRON

8 letters
FEVERFEW
PURSLANE

9 letters
CHAMOMILE
CORIANDER
CRANBERRY
DANDELION

11 letters
MARSH-MALLOW

14 letters
STINGING NETTLE

Wordsearch: TEA

Can you find all of the listed words hidden in the grid?
They may run forward or backward, in either a
horizontal, vertical or diagonal direction.

```
O O R X I J U A H C T A M U N
F E Y M Y N P R U A A S S A M
C N E W E C U I N M C H I N A
R I R X R S P I D E R L E G E
M M G T G B Q P Y R E W F N T
A S Y N L J I L D O I R U E I
T A D I R A O E E O M N G S H
U J A M A N L L N U U D N W
R J L R E I A L M I S V D I N
A I A E A T L L U T M E E G A
T P N P U N E A A D O O A R S
A A B P A N A B H B A Y M C D
Q K A E L N T N L Q R B L A P
P H B P R F C H U N M E E M C
R U S S I A N T K H R Y H B G
```

ASSAM	EARL GREY	JASMINE
BADULLA	GINSENG	LADY GREY
CAMEROON	GREEN	MATCHA UJI
CAMOMILE	HAPUTALE	MATURATA
CEYLON	HERBAL	PEPPERMINT
CHINA	HUNAN	RUSSIAN
CHUN MEE	INDIA	SPIDER LEG
DOOARS	JAPAN	WHITE

The words are provided, but can you fit them all in the grid?

4 letters
BEAR
KEEP
LAST
REST

5 letters
AWAIT
BROOK
DWELL
LODGE
TARRY

6 letters
ACCEPT
ENDURE
LIVE ON
RESIDE
SETTLE
SUFFER

7 letters
INHABIT
PERSIST
STOMACH
SURVIVE
SUSTAIN

8 letters
CONSTANT
FOOTHOLD
STAND FOR

9 letters
PERSEVERE

Can you find all of the listed words hidden in the grid?
They may run forward or backward, in either a
horizontal, vertical or diagonal direction.

```
L T A K E A R E S T U H O A I
G U S V S D X T C A T N A P L
H C L L N H A A N O D O F F A
L J A E U R U S L D X P K Y U
D N B L G M S T L E E F Z D N
N N R A M I B O E E R O G A W
U E Z H E D O E L Y H R Y Y I
T E K S F S O S R I E T V D N
U R T C E G K W U M S Y S R D
O A E N A U F S N A W W I E T
L R U P D L O N N G O I T A S
L P N O O I S O Y I R N B M N
I F Z F K S T O B N D K A V Y
H E W I Y Q E Z R E Z S C E S
C C E T A N R E B I H E K U R
```

CALM DOWN	IMAGINE	SLACKEN
CATNAP	LOOSEN UP	SLEEP
CHILL OUT	NOD OFF	SLUMBER
DAYDREAM	RELAX	SNOOZE
DOZE	REPOSE	STARGAZE
DROWSE	SHUT-EYE	TAKE A REST
FORTY WINKS	SIESTA	UNBEND
HIBERNATE	SIT BACK	UNWIND

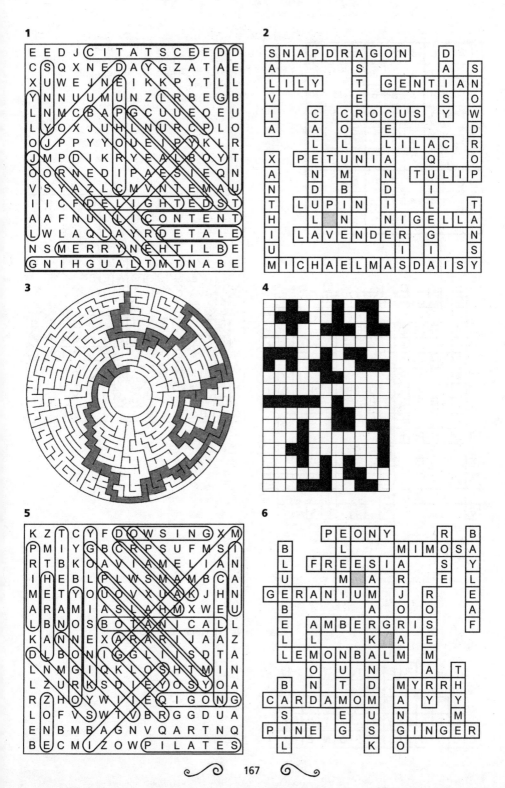

7

1	8	6	3	2	4	5	7	9
5	3	7	9	1	8	2	4	6
2	4	9	7	5	6	3	1	8
7	2	3	5	8	9	4	6	1
6	9	5	4	3	1	7	8	2
4	1	8	2	6	7	9	3	5
3	7	1	6	9	5	8	2	4
9	6	4	8	7	2	1	5	3
8	5	2	1	4	3	6	9	7

8

1 Tolerant, 2 Ornament, 3 Greatest,
4 Eyesight, 5 Thinnest, 6 Hazelnut, 7 Explicit,
8 Resident, 9 Novelist, 10 Elephant,
11 Schubert, 12 Shortcut.
Answer: TOGETHERNESS

9

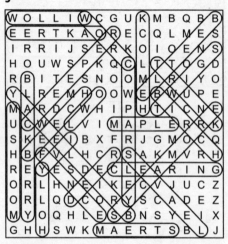

10

11

D: The chocolate stick is shorter.

12

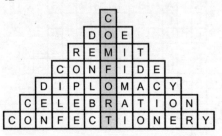

13

Nine-letters: COMMUNITY

SOLUTIONS

14

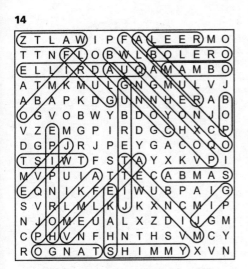

15

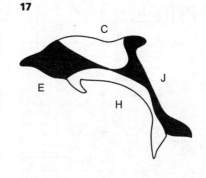

Answer: LOVE

16

Answer: ONWARD

17

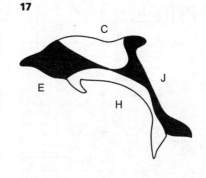

18

19

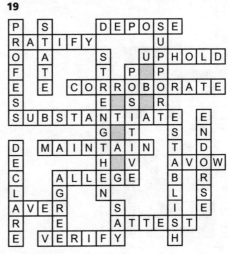

20

6	2	8	7	9	3	1	5	4
4	5	9	2	6	1	8	7	3
1	7	3	5	4	8	6	9	2
7	6	2	3	5	9	4	1	8
5	3	4	1	8	7	2	6	9
8	9	1	4	2	6	5	3	7
3	1	5	8	7	4	9	2	6
2	8	6	9	3	5	7	4	1
9	4	7	6	1	2	3	8	5

21

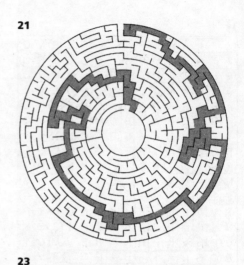

22

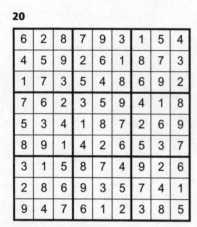

23

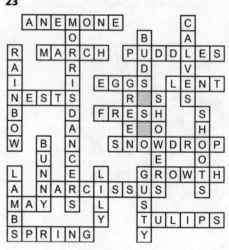

24

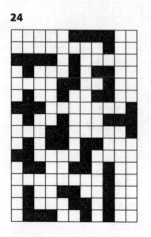

25

Answer: SWALLOWTAIL

26

```
D E N R A E L S U O R O G I V
R C S G A Z R N O Y N A C E T
C D E V R E S E R I O U S A P
V I V I D P T E V P D N D R M
D I X K E Y V U A E E E O Q V
S U B G N M G S T T S F K M H
I U X A T Z S N N S O K H J G
F P O M S I K I O U A E A N G
G H N R O S E R N R A D I E N
N R Z N O R G D O R T P S M I
I T A Y G N K P T T A S A E N
W T X V E O O F U G O X B Y W
E I D H E B E S L W R V Y T A
L S S S E L M O H T A F S X Y
A L O K T Y N T N A N O S E R
```

27

28

1 Pakistan, 2 Imprison, 3 Grandson,
4 Eviction, 5 Occasion, 6 Nitrogen,
7 Gershwin, 8 Optician, 9 Donation,
10 Watchman, 11 Illusion, 12 Tungsten.
Answer: PIGEON and GODWIT

29

C	L	A	V	I	C	L	E
T	O	L	E	R	A	T	E
T	A	L	I	S	M	A	N
M	U	S	H	R	O	O	M
D	I	P	L	O	M	A	T
S	H	I	L	L	I	N	G
N	I	C	H	O	L	A	S
N	E	E	D	L	E	S	S

30

```
C H G I S A I A H Y L E T M J
A E T N L B R G P W S S G O X
L U N I D S U S E J G Z H O R
V S G E M I H D N A G N F M C
I E R M M S G L D N T A M M L
N B A O Z Q O P O H J F A U M
L I H H X Y E H E I H A Z G
G U A K O N R B O M A P O T W
X S M L O E A U W R T R E O P
Q J A S H P S E B S O I L A W
X O N K T M M A G A V S R L A
Y M H I O Z U K S Q E H W U O
C L S S O W S T K Y A S F W R
V T E L B L E Q N M O Z J V F
A S E W X R U S S E L L M S M
```

31

32

Answer: BLUEBELL

33

Answer: CALENDULA

34

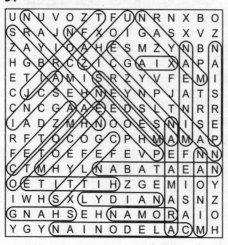

35

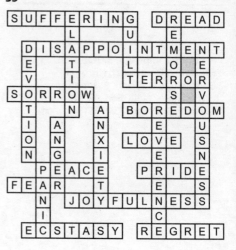

36

7	3	1	4	2	6	5	9	8
9	4	8	5	1	3	7	2	6
5	2	6	9	8	7	1	4	3
1	7	3	8	6	9	2	5	4
2	6	4	3	5	1	9	8	7
8	5	9	2	7	4	3	6	1
4	1	5	6	3	2	8	7	9
3	9	2	7	4	8	6	1	5
6	8	7	1	9	5	4	3	2

37

C	A	T	M	I	N	T
S	A	F	F	R	O	N
F	L	Y	T	R	A	P
N	I	G	E	L	L	A
A	L	K	A	N	E	T
B	U	G	B	A	N	E
L	U	C	E	R	N	E

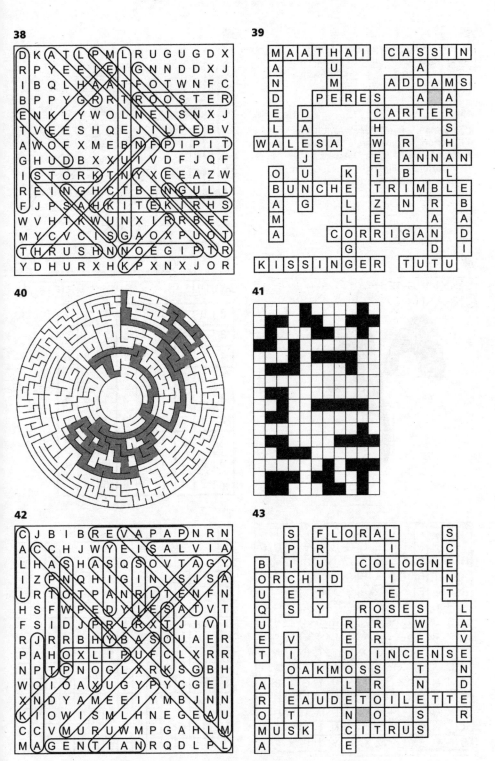

44

A: There is one more piece of fruit.

46

1 Salesman, 2 Pantheon, 3 Ambition,
4 Reaction, 5 Romanian, 6 Oblivion,
7 Wastebin, 8 Religion, 9 Assassin,
10 Vacation, 11 Einstein, 12 Napoleon.
Answer: SPARROW and RAVEN

47

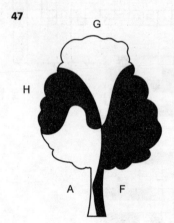

G
H
A   F

45

S	E	A	V	X	V	P	G	E	T	J	J	V	C	E
D	T	A	T	B	D	X	Y	J	G	D	K	I	E	S
A	A	U	J	E	B	E	V	R	E	D	N	O	W	U
S	P	N	D	O	R	L	L	D	L	V	U	H	X	M
C	I	P	O	Y	X	E	U	I	E	X	F	J	Y	E
E	C	H	R	P	E	C	V	N	B	S	H	E	D	D
R	I	I	Q	A	E	N	T	O	B	E	V	O	V	I
T	N	N	Z	F	I	E	I	L	I	R	R	S	Z	T
A	A	F	S	E	W	S	L	M	U	L	O	A	K	A
I	U	E	F	S	X	E	E	S	A	S	U	O	T	T
N	U	R	B	S	E	P	I	F	O	X	O	M	E	B
E	T	A	G	I	T	S	E	V	N	I	E	L	B	C
J	M	X	P	A	S	X	S	C	E	G	I	K	V	T
J	K	C	O	T	S	E	K	A	T	R	H	D	Y	E
Z	J	N	L	T	C	E	L	L	O	C	E	R	T	Z

48

3	9	5	6	8	7	4	1	2
8	6	1	2	4	5	9	3	7
4	7	2	9	3	1	5	8	6
1	3	9	4	5	6	2	7	8
6	5	7	8	2	3	1	9	4
2	4	8	7	1	9	3	6	5
5	1	6	3	7	4	8	2	9
9	8	3	5	6	2	7	4	1
7	2	4	1	9	8	6	5	3

49

S	S	D	L	L	F	C	H	T	D	K	W	C	T	G
T	Z	P	W	J	C	E	D	G	R	A	E	G	D	R
N	D	R	O	T	I	U	R	F	T	A	R	N	M	T
A	C	T	B	N	T	K	B	E	N	M	Y	I	R	E
R	L	F	E	Y	G	R	R	U	A	E	X	L	A	M
R	H	U	A	Q	E	E	D	E	T	E	A	L	G	P
U	B	U	T	C	N	S	R	B	R	T	S	I	U	E
C	P	P	I	A	H	C	A	Q	P	N	E	F	S	R
V	K	P	N	S	P	W	X	N	I	T	E	R	W	A
P	E	S	G	X	P	S	B	S	A	R	D	N	W	T
U	S	N	P	S	I	O	I	R	U	T	E	T	B	U
O	V	E	N	C	R	A	O	R	U	O	L	F	H	R
U	X	U	I	R	R	C	O	N	E	M	I	U	P	E
K	I	N	G	R	E	D	I	E	N	T	S	N	S	M
S	G	G	E	D	V	Z	Q	K	Y	J	F	X	F	X

50

Across / Down entries (crossword solution):

ROOFRACK, GUIDE, CANTEEN, CUTLERY, TORCH, WOOD, RAIN, OUTDOORS, KETTLE, ESCAPE, POLES, SITE, GRIDDLE, HATCHET, GROUNDSHEET

᎒᎐ SOLUTIONS ᎐᎒

51

D and H

52

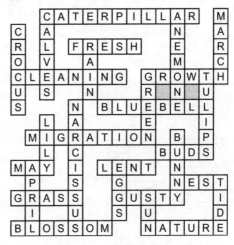

53

Nine-letters: WELLBEING

54

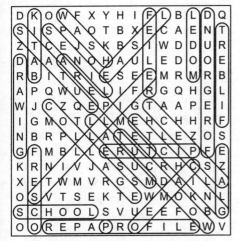

55

56

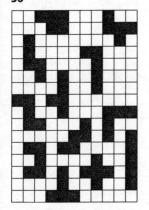

57

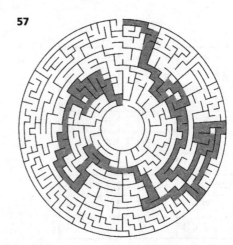

SOLUTIONS

58

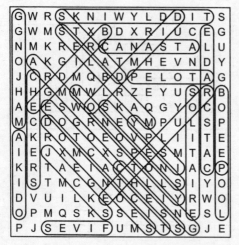

59

60

		C	E	A		
H	E	N	R	Y	F	O	R	D
	L	E	I		T		R
	A	R	T	I	S	T	I	C
S	P	O	I	L		O	V	A
	S		C	L	A	W	E	D
H	E	R	A		I		D
		L	A	S	T	L	Y
A	T	O	M	I	C		E
	A		A	M	O	R	A	L
B	U	G	S		P	A	C	E
	T		S	E	E	T	H	E

Answer: FAMILY

61

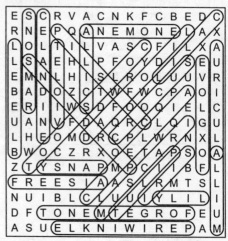

62

3	4	5	8	6	2	9	1	7
6	8	7	5	1	9	3	4	2
9	1	2	7	3	4	8	6	5
7	6	8	1	4	3	5	2	9
5	3	9	6	2	7	4	8	1
4	2	1	9	8	5	7	3	6
2	5	4	3	7	6	1	9	8
8	9	6	4	5	1	2	7	3
1	7	3	2	9	8	6	5	4

63

1 Brighter, 2 Engineer, 3 Armchair,
4 Calendar, 5 Hotelier, 6 Corridor, 7 Overhear,
8 Mediator, 9 Bachelor, 10 Interior,
11 November, 12 Gossamer.
Answer: BEACHCOMBING

64

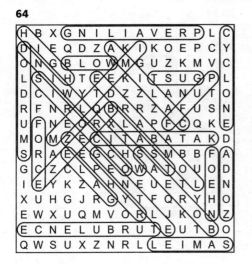

65

66

67

68

69

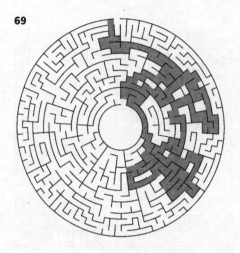

70

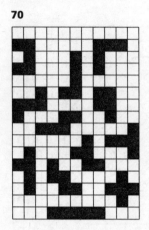

71

E	T	I	D	O	R	H	P	A	T	R	A	G	U	S
O	T	H	Q	C	T	A	Y	G	T	E	Q	I	H	A
H	W	B	E	A	U	T	I	F	U	L	N	L	C	F
A	Y	D	X	M	K	R	N	E	O	W	T	D	R	X
J	E	H	S	I	R	H	I	V	U	N	B	I	E	D
I	N	H	S	U	L	T	E	E	E	R	E	E	A	R
J	T	S	M	U	U	R	O	M	I	N	T	R	F	E
D	I	P	U	C	R	W	H	F	D	E	H	U	A	E
E	E	X	H	T	D	C	I	S	O	K	A	S	I	R
A	T	M	S	O	A	Q	H	T	L	X	N	A	R	I
N	D	N	O	T	K	I	T	T	E	N	D	E	E	S
G	D	R	T	T	P	K	N	T	N	O	S	R	S	E
E	K	A	K	W	I	D	O	G	T	V	O	T	T	D
L	H	E	Y	B	P	O	M	E	X	S	M	Q	H	U
I	L	Y	L	O	V	I	N	G	A	A	E	L	Z	Q

72

7	4	2	9	6	8	5	1	3
6	3	5	1	2	7	4	8	9
1	9	8	4	3	5	2	7	6
5	6	4	8	9	3	1	2	7
8	2	9	7	1	6	3	4	5
3	7	1	5	4	2	6	9	8
2	8	7	3	5	4	9	6	1
9	5	6	2	7	1	8	3	4
4	1	3	6	8	9	7	5	2

73

G: One of her plaits is shorter.

74

Answer: REDWING

SOLUTIONS

75

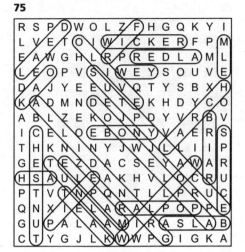

76

A	P	R	I	C	O	T			R		T			F
	E		L				L	E	M	O	N			O
M	A	N	G	O				D		F				R
	C		T				C	O	F	F	E	E		E
	H		T				U		E					S
C			E		S	H	E	R	B	E	T			T
A			D		O		R		A					F
P			C		N		N		K					R
P	U		R		P	E	A	N	U	T				U
C		C	H	E	R	R	Y		T					I
C			A		A				K					T
C	A	R	A	M	E	L			L	I	M	E		S
I					I			W						
N		R	U	M	A	N	D	R	A	I	S	I	N	
O					E									

77

C	H	E	R	V	I	L
M	A	Y	W	E	E	D
L	O	B	E	L	I	A
R	H	U	B	A	R	B
O	R	E	G	A	N	O
M	O	R	I	N	G	A
A	N	E	M	O	N	E

78

1 Ancestry, 2 Pharmacy, 3 Priority,
4 Recovery, 5 Equality, 6 Currency, 7 Identify,
8 Amicably, 9 Tendency, 10 Intimacy,
11 Ordinary, 12 Nativity.
Answer: APPRECIATION

79

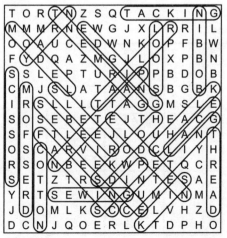

80

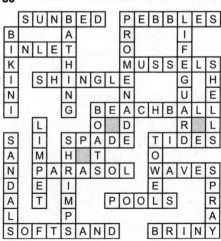

SOLUTIONS

81

Answer: NICOTIANA

82

|B|A|S|I|C| |M|A|C|A|Q|U|E|
|E| |H| |H| |I| |A| |U| |N|
|E|M|E|R|A|L|D| |S|T|I|N|G|
|C| |R| |P| |W| |H| |R| |R|
H	A	I	L		B	A	D		O	K	R	A
		F		J	O	Y		R				V
I	N	F	L	U	X		Z	O	M	B	I	E
N			G		P	I	T		R			
S	E	A	M		C	A	P		G	A	L	E
P		M		F		R		F		V		V
E	R	A	S	E		S	A	U	S	A	G	E
C		Z		E		O		S		D		N
T	R	E	A	S	O	N		S	C	O	U	T

Answer: CABBAGE WHITE

83

84

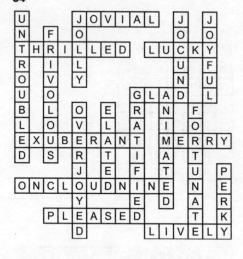

85

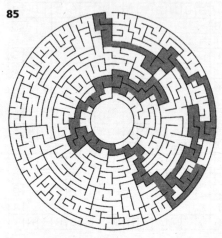

86

5	1	8	3	9	2	4	7	6
4	6	2	7	5	1	3	9	8
7	9	3	8	6	4	1	2	5
6	4	5	2	7	3	8	1	9
2	7	1	6	8	9	5	4	3
8	3	9	1	4	5	7	6	2
1	8	6	5	2	7	9	3	4
3	2	4	9	1	8	6	5	7
9	5	7	4	3	6	2	8	1

180

87

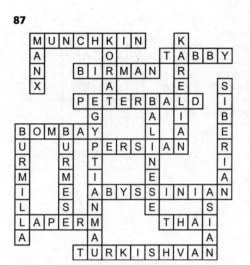

88

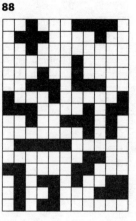

89

Answer: LARKSPUR

90

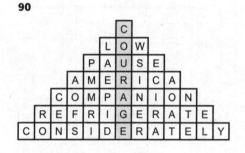

91

Nine-letters: ABUNDANCE

92

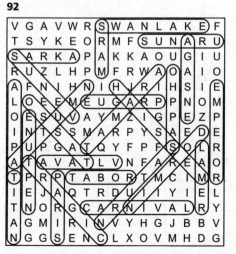

93

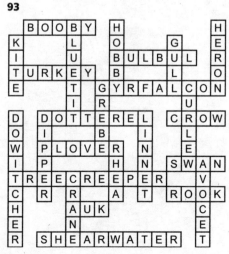

94

	P		C		S		D	
	S	O	R	C	E	R	E	R
D	I	R	E		R		L	
		N	E	M	E	S	I	S
	T	A	L	E	N	T		I
		T		T	E	R	S	E
A	R	E	A			A	U	G
	E		D		G	Y	B	E
B	A	L	L	S			Z	
	S	U	I		P	R	E	Y
	O	R	B		A	U	R	A
O	N	E		E	L	B	O	W

Answer: INTIMACY

95

1 Fabulous, 2 Idleness,
3 Nauseous, 4 Cerberus,
5 Hercules, 6 Reptiles, 7 Ellipsis,
8 Damascus, 9 Warriors,
10 Illinois, 11 Nowadays,
12 Goslings.
Answer: FINCH and REDWING

96

B	A	C	H	E	L	O	R
S	A	Y	O	N	A	R	A
V	I	C	T	O	R	I	A
O	N	L	O	O	K	E	R
T	R	A	V	E	S	T	Y
H	O	M	E	S	P	U	N
O	V	E	R	T	U	R	N
S	A	N	S	K	R	I	T

97

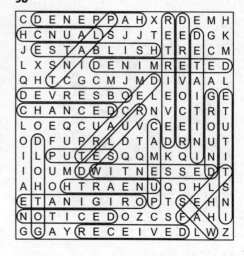

98

99

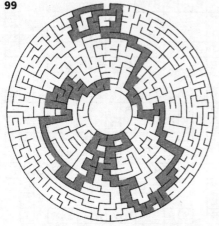

100

4	3	2	8	9	6	1	5	7
1	8	6	5	4	7	3	2	9
5	7	9	1	3	2	4	8	6
3	5	8	6	2	4	7	9	1
6	9	4	7	1	5	8	3	2
2	1	7	3	8	9	6	4	5
8	6	3	9	5	1	2	7	4
9	4	1	2	7	3	5	6	8
7	2	5	4	6	8	9	1	3

101

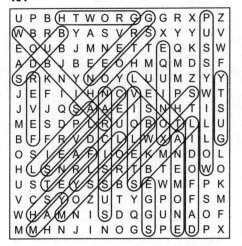

102

103

104

105

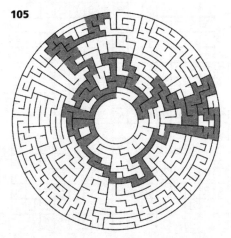

106

F: One of the apples is missing.

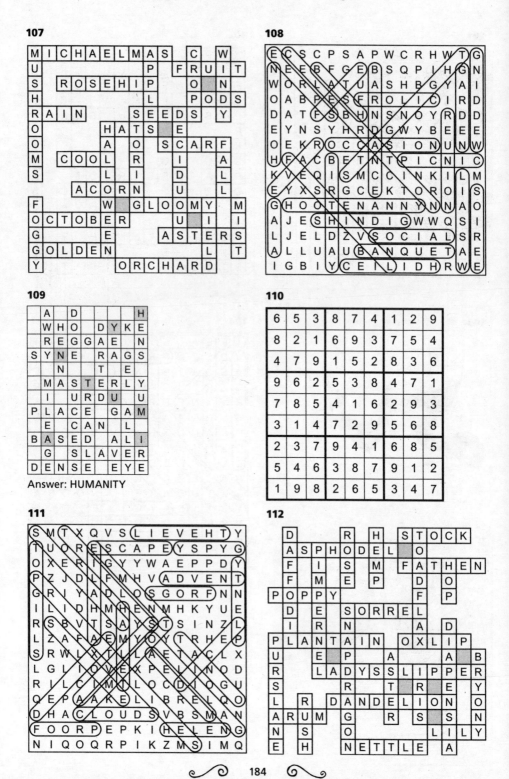

107

108

109

Answer: HUMANITY

110

111

112

SOLUTIONS

113

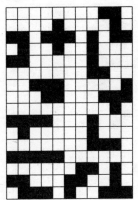

114

1 Raincoat, 2 Obedient, 3 Bankrupt,
4 Ignorant, 5 Nutrient, 6 Jubilant,
7 Argument, 8 Catapult, 9 Kilowatt,
10 Derelict, 11 Aircraft, 12 Wormcast.
Answer: ROBIN and JACKDAW

115

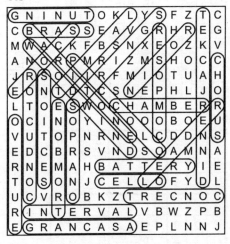

116

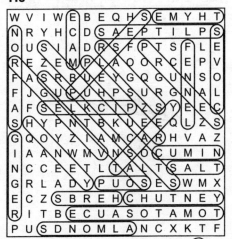

117

B and I

118

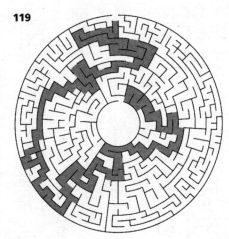

119

120

C		R	E	P	E	A	T		R		P
A		H		U				S	P	O	O	L
S	W	E	A	T	E	R		W		W		A
T		N		L		Y	A	R	N	S		I
O		K	J		P			I		Y		N
N		S	Q	U	A	R	E	S		L		

121

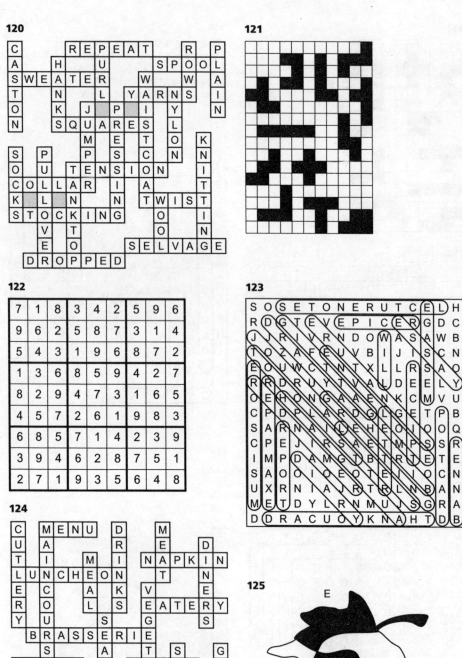

122

7	1	8	3	4	2	5	9	6
9	6	2	5	8	7	3	1	4
5	4	3	1	9	6	8	7	2
1	3	6	8	5	9	4	2	7
8	2	9	4	7	3	1	6	5
4	5	7	2	6	1	9	8	3
6	8	5	7	1	4	2	3	9
3	9	4	6	2	8	7	5	1
2	7	1	9	3	5	6	4	8

123

124

125

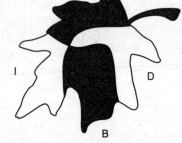

126

S	O	U	R	S	O	P
S	P	U	R	R	E	Y
P	R	I	M	U	L	A
B	R	I	N	J	A	L
H	E	N	B	A	N	E
L	A	C	T	U	C	A
T	U	R	P	E	T	H

127

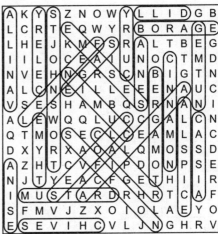

128

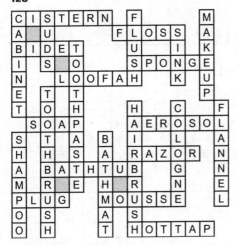

129

Answer: BRAMLEY

130

1 Language, 2 Immunize (or Immunise),
3 Nail file, 4 Necklace, 5 Everyone, 6 Tenerife,
7 Mandible, 8 Adequate, 9 Graduate,
10 Paradise, 11 Insulate, 12 Embezzle.
Answer: LINNET and MAGPIE

131

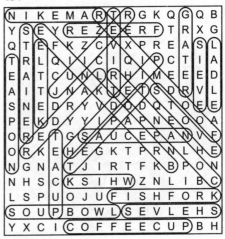

132

133

Nine-letters: ENJOYMENT

134

	A	I		A	B
P	A	N	C	E	T	T	A
I	T	S		L	L
N	A	M	E	P	L	A	T	E
	R		C	R	I	S	I	S
S	Y	S	T	E	M		C
		T		S	A	C	K	S
A	G	R	E	E		A		T
	L	I	S	T	E	N	E	R
C	A	P	S		K	I	W	I
	N	E	A	T	E	N	E	D
E	D	D	Y		S	E	R	E

Answer: DANCING

135

9	3	6	7	1	8	5	2	4
1	8	2	3	5	4	7	6	9
4	7	5	6	2	9	1	8	3
2	9	3	4	6	5	8	1	7
6	5	4	8	7	1	3	9	2
7	1	8	2	9	3	4	5	6
3	4	9	1	8	2	6	7	5
8	2	7	5	4	6	9	3	1
5	6	1	9	3	7	2	4	8

136

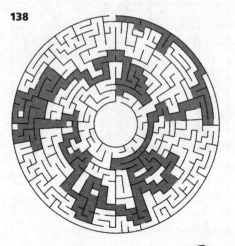

137

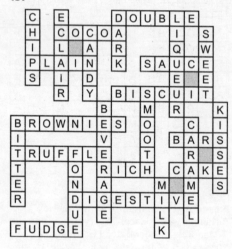

138

139

SOLUTIONS

140

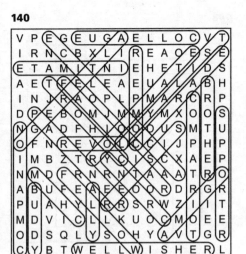

141

142

Answer: PEACOCK

143

H: One trail of melted wax is longer.

144

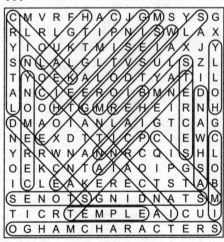

145

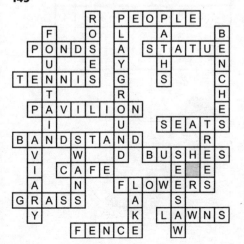

146

F	L	O	W	E	R	E	D
D	E	X	T	R	O	S	E
J	E	T	T	I	S	O	N
P	R	O	G	R	E	S	S
C	I	N	N	A	M	O	N
V	I	G	I	L	A	N	T
S	Q	U	I	R	R	E	L
A	M	E	T	H	Y	S	T

189

147

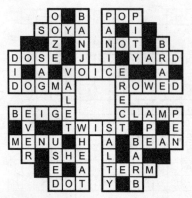

Answer: PANSY

148

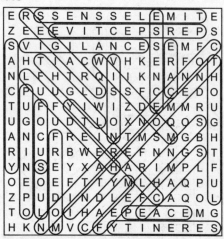

149

Answer: FOXGLOVE

150

1 Adequate, 2 Untangle, 3 Tortoise,
4 Handsome, 5 Estimate, 6 Nonsense,
7 Take care, 8 Infinite, 9 Commence,
10 Increase, 11 Triangle, 12 Yosemite.
Answer: AUTHENTICITY

151

8	5	7	6	1	2	9	3	4
6	4	9	7	5	3	8	1	2
3	2	1	4	8	9	7	5	6
4	8	6	9	2	5	1	7	3
9	1	2	3	7	6	4	8	5
7	3	5	1	4	8	2	6	9
5	9	8	2	6	7	3	4	1
1	7	3	5	9	4	6	2	8
2	6	4	8	3	1	5	9	7

152

153

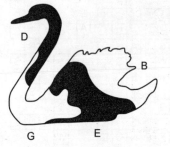

SOLUTIONS

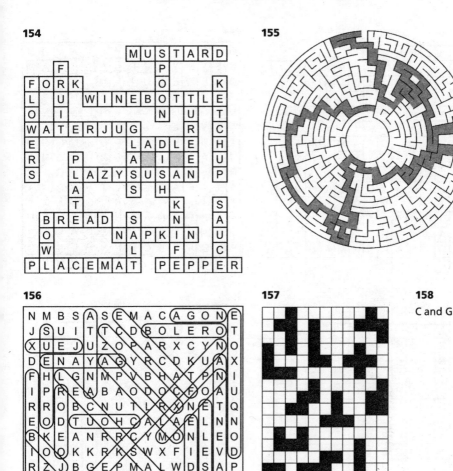

154

155

156

157

158

C and G

159

Answer: SHIREN

160

161

Nine-letters: BELONGING

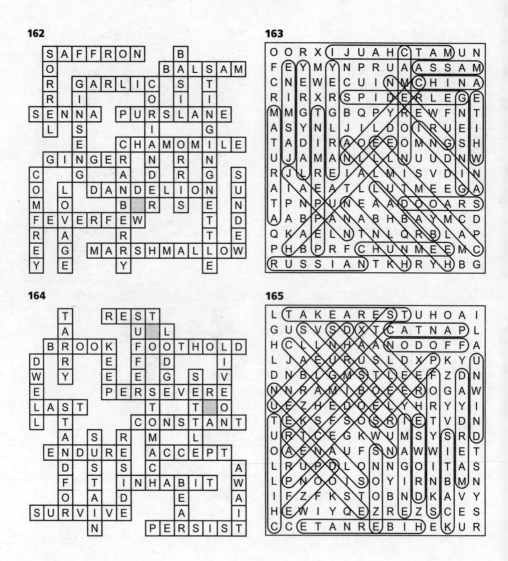

162

163

164

165